# INTERACTING

## WITH

# GOD

*in Ephesians 1-3*

GENE A. GETZ
CLAUDE V. KING

BACK TO THE BIBLE®
*Publishing*

Back to the Bible Publishing
P.O. Box 82808
Lincoln, NE  68501

For information about language translations, international availability, and licensing for non-English publication, contact Back to the Bible Publishing at the above address.

Additional copies of this book are available from Back to the Bible Publishing. You may order by calling 1-888-559-7878 or visiting our Web site at www.InteractingWithGod.org.

1 2 3 4 5 6 7 8 9 10—03 02 01 00 99 98

ISBN 0-8474-0200-2

Printed in the USA

# CONTENTS

# WELCOME

## Meet Your Bible Study Leaders

*Dr. Gene A. Getz* is senior pastor of Fellowship Bible Church North in Plano, Texas. He also is the director of the Center for Church Renewal, host for the *Renewal* radio program, and author of near-  ly 50 books, including *The Walk, The Measure of a Man*, and *Building Up One An- other*.

*Claude V. King* is a writer and conference speaker. He is coau-  thor of many discipleship courses, includ- ing *Experienc- ing God, The Mind of Christ, Fresh Encounter, In God's Presence*, and *Break Down the Walls*.

*W*elcome to our Bible study time together. We are looking forward to serving you as you seek to know, understand, and apply God's Word to your life. As you spend time in God's Word each week, we will be your personal Bible study leaders.

Through the years, people have responded to God's Word in different ways. Some have taken a human-centered approach, where they focus on their own human rea- soning to decide what is right and wrong. They don't spend much time seeking to know what God has to say in His Word. This was the way of the Sadducees. Jesus said to them, "You do not know the Scriptures or the power of God" (Mark 12:24).

Others take a Word-centered approach to Scripture. They study the Bible carefully and then try to live their lives by what they read. Though this sounds good, it falls short of God's very best. Jesus said to the Jewish leaders, "You diligently study the Scriptures because you think that by them you possess eternal life. . . . yet you refuse to come to me to have life" (John 5:39-40). Trying to live God's Word without an in- timate relationship with Him can become mechanical, empty, legalistic, and frustrat- ing. God has so much more in store for your life and for your church than this.

God's very best is a Christ-centered approach to the Scriptures. In this approach you study the Bible carefully and then take one more step into a personal and intimate love relationship with Jesus Christ. Jesus said, "These are the Scriptures that testify about me . . . come to me to have life" (John 5:39-40). God created you for a love relationship with Him. The Bible is God's Word that tells you about Him and then invites you into an intimate and personal love relationship with Him through Jesus Christ. This is where you experience life to its fullest. This is what we desire for you. We want to help you study God's Word and then take the next step to a dynamic re- lationship with God and with God's people—the church.

Interacting with God is a series of Bible study tools designed to help you study God's Word and then respond to God as you develop your personal relationship with Him. We will assist you and your small group in your study and application of God's Word. We will help you interact with each other and with God so you can experience the full dimensions of being a healthy and loving part of the Body of Christ. We pray that you will experience God's best in your personal relationship with Him and in your experience as a part of a healthy Body of Christ—your church.

*Gene A. Getz*
*Claude V. King*

# INTRODUCTION TO INTERACTING WITH GOD

**Note:** If you already have studied another *Interacting with God* Bible study workbook, you may review the following introduction or skip to page 13, Part 4, to begin. If this is your first time to use an *Interacting with God* workbook, you'll want to read and work through this introduction to get the most out of your study.

## PART 1: PERSONAL AND SMALL-GROUP BIBLE STUDY

This workbook is one course in a series of Bible study tools developed to help Christians experience a dynamic relationship with God. New courses in this series will be released regularly to help you accomplish two primary goals. While studying a course:

1. You will know and understand what God is saying to you in the Bible text studied, and you'll experience an increasingly intimate love relationship with Him.

2. Together with other Christians, you will grow in your love for one another and increasingly become a healthy and mature Body of Christ that brings glory to God.

Those goals may sound too high or unreachable to you. And indeed, we're not able to accomplish them in our human abilities. Only God can lead His people in such a way that these two goals can be accomplished in your life and in your church. That's why we will be pointing you through the Scriptures to the Lord. As you interact with Him and His Word, God Himself will guide you and your group to experience His best. He will be speaking to you and working in your lives in ways we would never even think about. The coming months will be a spiritual adventure as God opens your minds to understand and apply His Word to your lives, your families, your church, your community, and your world.

If you're not a Christian, don't stop now. We want to help you come to know more about God, so stay with us. This study will help you see more about the kind of love relationship He desires to have with you. We will occasionally ask you to examine your relationship with God, knowing that He will be working in your life to reveal Himself and draw you to His Son, Jesus Christ. Being in a small group with Christians will give you a chance to see up close the difference God makes in a life.

This *Interacting with God* course has two primary parts. One is a self-paced Bible study that you complete on your own. The second is a minichurch meeting where you will join with other believers to become the kind of healthy Body of Christ that God desires. First, let us explain the self-paced Bible study for you.

## SELF-PACED BIBLE STUDY

Each week you'll have a nine-page lesson to study prior to meeting with your small group (minichurch). Each lesson has been divided into four parts so you can study the lesson over a period of several days. Since each part includes a study of God's Word and a time for prayer and interacting with God, you may want to use this as your daily devotional guide. You'll need to complete your study of the lesson prior to your minichurch meeting, <u>because the content will not be repeated</u> during that time. If you're not able to complete a lesson during the week, however, you'll still want to come to the minichurch meeting. Get started on your lesson early in the week so you'll have time to complete it and begin applying it to your life prior to meeting with your minichurch. The study has several features:

**1. Learning Activities.** We (Gene and Claude) are going to be your personal Bible study leaders. As we introduce you to some information, we'll ask you a question or guide you to process what you're learning. If there's one correct answer to the question, we'll tell you what it is so you can make sure you are understanding what you're studying. This is not a test to be graded (although you would probably make an A if it were). It's a dialogue with us. We hope you'll enjoy the interactive way we lead you in your study.

► **Learning activities look like this. They begin with an arrow and bold-faced text that is indented from the main text. Turn to page 9 and find Activity 4 to see what they will look like. Check this box when you've found this activity.** ❑

Did you complete the activity? Although this one above isn't very important, the others will be helpful to you. If you don't complete them, you'll miss out on the greater value of this workbook, and you'll be less prepared for your minichurch meeting. We encourage you not to skip the learning activities.

**2. Scripture Reading.** In Part 1 of each lesson, you'll be given an assignment to read or listen to a portion of Scripture. We've given you several options, from one chapter to the whole Book of Ephesians (six chapters). You'll benefit from being familiar with the whole message of the book as we turn our study to one small part of the message. Audio versions of the Bible are available at Christian bookstores. You might prefer listening to the passage being read. You might even want to listen to it several times during the course while driving in your car or some other time. We encourage you to read or listen to the entire Book of Ephesians in the first or second week of your study. It will probably take you from 15 to 30 minutes, depending on how fast you read.

**3. Memorizing Scripture.** In Part 1 of each lesson you will be directed to work on memorizing Scripture. The psalmist said, "Your word is a lamp to my feet and a light for my path" and "I have hidden your word in my heart that I might not sin against you" (Ps. 119:105, 11). Memorizing God's Word has great value for your life in Christ.

➤ Turn to the last page of this book and tear out the perforated bookmark in the upper-left corner of the page. You can use it to keep up with your place in the workbook.

One side of the bookmark has tips for memorizing Scripture. As you begin to learn a new verse, review the tips and practice them during the week. Decide on your own pace for memorizing verses. We have provided 12 scriptures on the perforated cards in the back of the book. Each of these passages comes from Ephesians 1–3. One side of the card has the passage in the New International Version, and the other side has it in the much-loved King James Version. You may choose either one and then pick one of the following options or determine your own pace.
- ❑ One scripture each week
- ❑ One scripture every other week
- ❑ One scripture each month

Occasionally during your minichurch meetings, you'll have an opportunity to recite the verse you're memorizing and state what it has come to mean to you.

**4. Scriptures.** Throughout the workbook, we have provided the text for most of the scriptures we use or make reference to. This is to save you time in your study. We also know many people don't take time to look up scriptures that are only referenced. We want you to read God's Word, because God uses it to speak to you. The scriptures are the most important words in this book. As you read scriptures that are especially meaningful to you, you may want to turn to them in your Bible and underline them for future reference.

**5. Main Column and Margin.** The primary column for your study is the wide one on the right side of each page. Always start reading and studying in that column. We use

the left margin as a place for reference. Some activities will direct you to scriptures or lists that appear in the margin. Sometimes we provide a summary list in the margin for quick reference. Occasionally we'll place an important statement in the margin. In those cases, they are always quotes from the main column. Some activities will ask you to write something in the margin. Usually we'll provide you with lines to write on when they're required. You also can use the margin to write your own study notes.

**6. Interacting with God.** A praying hands icon will be used throughout this workbook to alert you to an invitation to spend time with God. During these times, you will talk to God in prayer in a variety of ways.

 Let's begin right now. Spend a moment in prayer as you begin this course. Ask God to open your mind to understand the Scriptures. Give Him permission to work in your life, family, and church. Tell Him about your desire to know and experience a love relationship with Him.

Did you spend time with God in prayer? If you didn't, go back and take a moment now. If you complete this workbook and don't take time to be with God, the information will be of little help to you. We don't want you just to know about God. We want you to experience Him in a dynamic and personal relationship. Spending time with Him in prayer will be a key part of your experience.

## MINICHURCH MEETINGS

Does something seem to be missing in your church experience? Many people today would answer yes. But they're not quite sure what's missing. They just know there ought to be more. They read the New Testament and realize that the first-century church experienced more. Many people have tried to describe what's missing. We believe one major need is for the experience of "body life."

Many churches have become much more like an organization than a body. God intended that we function as a close-knit, loving, caring community of believers. Though corporate worship is an important and meaningful part of being the Body of Christ, large-group events don't provide opportunities for members to give and receive love.

Thus, what's needed is the combination of large- and small-group experiences enjoyed by the early church:
- "Every day they continued to meet together in the *temple courts*. They broke bread *in their homes* and ate together with glad and sincere hearts, praising God and enjoying the favor of all the people. And the Lord added to their number daily those who were being saved" (Acts 2:46-47).

- "Day after day, in the *temple courts* and from *house to house*, they never stopped teaching and proclaiming the good news that Jesus is the Christ" (Acts 5:42).

What's often missing, however, is a small-group setting in which Christians can become part of a loving and sharing community of believers. We call this small group a minichurch (a little church within the church). A minichurch could go by many other names:

- Sunday school class
- discipleship class
- home Bible study group
- cell group
- house church
- midweek Bible study
- men's ministry group
- women's ministry group

A minichurch could even be a family. It's simply a small group of Christians that meets regularly to experience the unity and love God intended for the Body of Christ. These believers will be able to carry out many of the functions of the church far more effectively than a large group can.

Thus, we have designed this study for use in small-group settings. We will call your small groups minichurches, but you can call them whatever is most appropriate for your setting. Just keep in mind that your small group needs to function like the church to one another in every way the Holy Spirit leads you. As small groups experience renewal in their walk together with Christ, churches will begin to experience renewal in their effectiveness as a larger body—both in ministry to one another and in outreach to a lost world.

**Leadership of the Minichurch.** We recommend that each group have a leader and a leader apprentice or two coleaders. The leader does not have to be a content expert. All members will study the content of this workbook in preparation for the meetings. The leader will be a spiritual facilitator who guides the members to function as the Body of Christ to one another. The focus will be on building meaningful relationships around the truths of God's Word.

The apprentice (or coleader) is a leader in training. As your minichurch grows, it will need to multiply to two groups. This will allow the groups to stay small enough so members can maintain spiritual intimacy with one another. When this multiplication occurs, half of the group will go with the leader, and the apprentice will become leader of the other half. Then each of the new groups will secure a new apprentice. We've provided more detailed helps in the "Minichurch Leader's Guide," beginning on page 135.

**Group Size.** Since the purpose of the minichurch is to allow for close relationships between believers, the group can't grow too large without hindering the spiritual intimacy. The leadership team will need to monitor size and intimacy to determine the times to multiply. A group that reaches 16-20 believers in regular attendance is probably ready to multiply.

**Composition.** Though the minichurch is for believers, it's also a wonderful place for non-Christians to see the love and unity of God's people up close. Under the teaching of God's Word in a loving atmosphere, many will come to Christ. You should feel free to invite unsaved people to attend the minichurch meetings and participate in the Bible study by using this workbook. Once they come to Christ, the minichurch will be a wonderful setting to help them become mature disciples.

**Meeting Time and Place.** Minichurches can meet at almost any place and time. We recommend allowing one and one-half to two hours for your minichurch meetings. This will allow for quality time together. Probably by the time you read this introduction, time and place have been set. The leader's guide provides more help if you need counsel.

**Meeting Activities.** We want you to let God be in charge of your meetings. His Spirit can guide you to experience His best for your group. We will be providing suggestions for your leader. Since members will complete their personal Bible study during the week, the minichurch meeting can adjust to God's agenda. This is where the body life of the church can take place. You will want to pray regularly for your leader. Ask the Holy Spirit to guide your leader so the minichurch will experience God's best and bring glory and pleasure to Him.

## Part 2: Bad News and Good News

As you begin (or as you participate in) this study, you may realize you do not have a right relationship with God. You may have an emptiness or void in your life that you can't seem to fill. You may be captive to sin and know of no way out. You may see that believing Christians have a relationship with God that's different from what you're experiencing. You may see their love, joy, and peace and long for such a life. If you're not a Christian, or if you have doubts about whether you have ever been "saved" or "born again," you need to understand how you can be changed forever by a saving relationship with Jesus Christ. We want to help you. This part of the introduction is to help you:

- understand why you need a Savior.
- understand the good news about Jesus Christ and how He can save you.
- hear God's call or invitation for you to repent of your sins and turn to a love relationship with God through His Son, Jesus Christ.

For those of you who do have a saving relationship with Jesus Christ, this part of the lesson may help you be prepared to tell others the way to saving faith in Christ. As you study it, you can review your own experience of God's saving grace. It may even help you to better understand what God has done in your life. Allow the Lord to remind you of His mighty work that has changed your life.

**Deuteronomy 6:4-5**

"Hear, O Israel: The Lord our God, the Lord is one. Love the Lord your God with all your heart and with all your soul and with all your strength."

**Jeremiah 31:3**

"The Lord appeared to us in the past, saying: 'I have loved you with an everlasting love; I have drawn you with loving-kindness.'"

**Hosea 11:4**

"I led them with cords of human kindness, with ties of love."

**John 14:21**

"'Whoever has my commands and obeys them, he is the one who loves me. He who loves me will be loved by my Father, and I too will love him and show myself to him.'"

**John 14:23**

"Jesus replied, 'If anyone loves me, he will obey my teaching. My Father will love him, and we will come to him and make our home with him.'"

🖑 As you begin, ask God to open your mind to understand how a person can have an intimate love relationship with Him.

God created us for a love relationship with Him. When God first created Adam and Eve, He spent time with them in the garden in the cool of the day. He loved them, and they loved Him. But when they sinned against God's command, the love relationship was broken. Ever since that time, God has been calling sinful people to return to a right relationship with Him.

➤1. **Read the scriptures in the margin, and circle the words** *love,* *loved,* **and** *loving.*

God wants a love relationship with everyone. But sin separates people from Him. We don't have to sin much to be a sinner, either: "For whoever keeps the whole law and yet stumbles at just one point is guilty of breaking all of it. . . . you have become a law-breaker" (James 2:10-11). According to God, "All have sinned and fall short of the glory of God" (Rom. 3:23).

➤2. **Would you agree with God that you are a sinner, that you fall short of the perfect glory of God?**     ❏ Yes    ❏ No

If you don't agree, one or more of the following may be true:
- You don't know the commands and requirements of God that you have violated.
- You don't know or understand God's perfection that sets the standard for measuring your life.
- Your pride won't allow you to admit you don't measure up to God's standard of perfection.
- You have deceived yourself into believing you've never sinned and broken fellowship with God.
- You don't believe there is a God who has the right to set a standard to measure your life.

If you won't agree with God that you're a sinner, you can't and won't take the necessary steps to enter into a saving, love relationship with Him. If you're struggling with this, there's some good news: "The Lord your God will circumcise your hearts and the hearts of your descendants, so that you may love him with all your heart and with all your soul, and live" (Deut. 30:6). God can replace your hard heart with a responsive one if you will turn to Him for help (Ezek. 36:26-27).

**Ezekiel 36:26-27**

"'I will give you a new heart and put a new spirit in you; I will remove from you your heart of stone and give you a heart of flesh. And I will put my Spirit in you and move you to follow my decrees and be careful to keep my laws.'"

**Ephesians 2:8-9**

"It is by grace you have been saved, through faith—and this not from yourselves, it is the gift of God—not by works, so that no one can boast."

**Titus 3:5**

"He saved us, not because of righteous things we had done, but because of his mercy."

**Bad News.** Once you agree with God that you're a sinner, there's some bad news: "The wages of sin is death" (Rom. 6:23). Because of your sin, you have been given a death penalty by a holy God. Paul described this spiritual death this way: You are "dead in your transgressions and sins" (Eph. 2:1), "separate from Christ, excluded from citizenship in Israel and foreigners to the covenants of the promise, without hope and without God in the world" (Eph. 2:12).

The bad news gets worse. According to God, you cannot save yourself. No amount of good works or acts of righteousness can remove your death penalty.

➤3. **Read Ephesians 2:8-9 and Titus 3:5 in the margin, and underline the words or phrases in each that describe what cannot save you.**

You can't save yourself. However, the news isn't all bad. What you can't do for yourself, God did for you through His Son, Jesus Christ.

"God so loved the world that he gave his one and only Son, that whoever believes in him shall not perish but have eternal life. For God did not send his Son into the world to condemn the world, but to save the world through him. Whoever believes in him is not condemned, but whoever does not believe stands condemned already because he has not believed in the name of God's one and only Son. . . .

"Whoever believes in the Son has eternal life, but whoever rejects the Son will not see life, for God's wrath remains on him" (John 3:16-18, 36).

➤4. **Based on what you just read in John 3:16-18 and 36, match the person on the left with the correct descriptions on the right. Write a number beside each letter.**

  1. One who believes in     ___a. shall not perish
      Christ the Son       ___b. is not condemned
                        ___c. is condemned already
  2. Unbeliever who rejects     ___d. has eternal life
      Christ the Son       ___e. will not see life
                        ___f. God's wrath remains on him

**Good News.** God loved the world (including you and us) so much that He gave His only Son to die on a cross for us. The gospel (the good news) is this: "Christ died for our sins according to the Scriptures, . . . he was buried, . . . he was raised on the third day according to the Scriptures" (1 Cor. 15:3-4). Those who believe and trust in what Christ has done are no longer condemned to death. They receive eternal life. (Answers: 1-a, b, d; 2-c, e, f).

Paul and his partner Silas had been beaten and thrown into prison in Philippi. They started singing hymns of praise to the Lord, and the jailer couldn't understand such joy. He realized they had something he didn't have in his life. When an earthquake brought on a crisis in his life, the jailer asked Paul and Silas, "Sirs, what must I do to be saved?" (Acts 16:30). That's a good question that you may be asking by now.

➤5. **In the following Scripture, underline their answer to his question.**

"They replied, 'Believe in the Lord Jesus, and you will be saved—you and your household.' Then they spoke the word of the Lord to him and to all the others in his house. . . . then immediately he and all his family were baptized. The jailer brought them into his house and set a meal before them; he was filled with joy because he had come to believe in God—he and his whole family" (Acts 16:31-34).

When the jailer and his family heard the good news about Jesus, they believed in Him and turned to Him to receive His saving grace. God saved the whole family that night, just as Jesus said He would. But you may ask, "How can Jesus' death pay the death penalty I owe?"

➤6. **Read in the margin Paul's description of what God has done to take care of your sin problem (Rom. 3:21-26). Then answer these questions:**

1. Since you aren't saved by your righteousness, where does an acceptable righteousness come from? (v. 21)

   _____

2. (Fill in the blank, v. 22) "This righteousness from God comes through faith in Jesus Christ to all who

   _____."

3. What did God present Jesus to be for us? (v. 25) "God presented him as a

   s_____ of a_____."

4. Why did God do this? (v. 25) "To demonstrate his _____."

5. Who are the ones God justifies (erases their death penalty just as if they had never sinned)? (v. 26)

   _____

**Romans 3:21-26**

²¹"Now a righteousness from God, apart from law, has been made known, to which the Law and the Prophets testify. ²²This righteousness from God comes through faith in Jesus Christ to all who believe. There is no difference, ²³for all have sinned and fall short of the glory of God, ²⁴and are justified freely by his grace through the redemption that came by Christ Jesus. ²⁵God presented him as a sacrifice of atonement, through faith in his blood. He did this to demonstrate his justice, because in his forbearance he had left the sins committed beforehand unpunished—²⁶he did it to demonstrate his justice at the present time, so as to be just and the one who justifies those who have faith in Jesus."

For those who have faith in Jesus and believe (or trust) in His sacrifice for their sins, God gives an acceptable righteousness. When Jesus died on the cross, He paid the death penalty for you. He died in your place as a "sacrifice of atonement." Because God is just, He had to punish sin. But because of His mercy, He paid the penalty Himself through the shed blood of Jesus. Those who place their faith in what Jesus has done are justified by God. They're restored to a right relationship with God just as if they had never sinned. "God made him who had no sin to be sin for us, so that in him we might become the righteousness of God" (2 Cor. 5:21). That's good news! According to the Bible, "Salvation is found in no one else, for there is no other name under heaven given to men by which we must be saved" (Acts 4:12).

🙏 Take a moment to thank God for providing His Son as a sacrifice so you could be set free from your death penalty.

The next part of this lesson will help you understand more fully how to experience salvation by faith in Jesus Christ. You may want to stop here and take up Part 3 tomorrow. However, if you sense God is speaking to you in a special way, go ahead and study Part 3 now.

## PART 3: CALLED TO SALVATION

In John 6:44, Jesus said, "No one can come to me unless the Father who sent me draws him." You cannot initiate salvation on your own. God must begin the process by drawing you to Himself. A number of scriptures indicate that we are called to salvation.

➤7. **Read the following scriptures, and underline the word *called* each time it occurs. We've underlined one for you.**

• "To all . . . who are loved by God and called to be saints" (Rom. 1:7).

- "God works for the good of those who love him, who have been called according to his purpose" (Rom. 8:28).
- "Brothers, think of what you were when you were called" (1 Cor. 1:26).
- "I pray also that the eyes of your heart may be enlightened in order that you may know the hope to which he has called you" (Eph. 1:18).
- "There is one body and one Spirit—just as you were called to one hope when you were called" (Eph. 4:4).
- "Take hold of the eternal life to which you were called" (1 Tim. 6:12).
- "Christ is the mediator of a new covenant, that those who are called may receive the promised eternal inheritance" (Heb. 9:15).
- "You are a chosen people, a royal priesthood, a holy nation, a people belonging to God, that you may declare the praises of him who called you out of darkness into his wonderful light" (1 Pet. 2:9).
- "The God of all grace, who called you to his eternal glory in Christ" (1 Pet. 5:10).
- "His divine power has given us everything we need for life and godliness through our knowledge of him who called us by his own glory and goodness" (2 Pet. 1:3).

God must draw you, and He must call you to salvation. He has already done all that's necessary to provide for your salvation. That good news about salvation, however, gets better, because we find that God already wants to draw you to Himself.

**1 Timothy 2:1-4**

"I urge, then, first of all, that requests, prayers, intercession and thanksgiving be made for everyone—for kings and all those in authority, that we may live peaceful and quiet lives in all godliness and holiness. This is good, and pleases God our Savior, who wants all men to be saved and to come to a knowledge of the truth."

**2 Peter 3:9**

"The Lord is not slow in keeping his promise, as some understand slowness. He is patient with you, not wanting anyone to perish, but everyone to come to repentance."

God is calling for you to come to Him.

➤**8. Read the Scriptures in the margin. Who are the ones God wants to bring to repentance so they will be saved? Check one.**

❑ a. God wants only the very best people to be saved.
❑ b. God wants only important people to be saved.
❑ c. God wants everyone to repent and be saved.
❑ d. God doesn't want anyone to be saved.

If you didn't check *c*, you need to read the scriptures again. God desires that everyone be saved and come to repentance. He wants to draw you to His Son. The very fact that you've gotten this far in this lesson may well be because the Father is drawing you to Himself.

➤**9. Are you at a point in your life where you desire to hear God's call to salvation? Do you want to experience the change He can bring about so you will experience life abundantly? Check your response.**

❑ a. Yes, I want to be saved and know the joy and abundant life God can give me.
❑ b. I'm interested, but I still have some questions and concerns I must deal with before I'm ready.
❑ c. No, that isn't my desire at this time.
❑ d. I don't have that desire, but I'm open to God giving me that desire if He chooses to.

If you desire that love relationship with God, there's a reason. "It is God who works in you to will and to act according to his good purpose" (Phil. 2:13). Through His Word as well, God is calling you to come to Him:

John 7:37-38—"If anyone is thirsty, let him come to me and drink. Whoever believes in me, as the Scripture has said, streams of living water will flow from within him."

Revelation 22:17—"The Spirit and the bride say, 'Come!' And let him who hears say, 'Come!' Whoever is thirsty, let him come; and whoever wishes, let him take the free gift of the water of life."

If you're thirsty—if you have a spiritual desire to come to Christ—you're invited! Jesus said, "Everyone who listens to the Father and learns from him comes to me" (John 6:45). We believe that during your study of God's Word, God Himself will begin to speak to you and teach you. He will draw you to Himself because He loves you and wants to have a dynamic relationship with you. If your heart and will are responsive, He will establish that love relationship with you. Like the Philippian jailer, you will be filled with joy because you have believed in Christ.

One day some people asked Jesus, "What must we do to do the works God requires?" And Jesus responded, "The work of God is this: to believe in the one he has sent" (John 6:28-29). In the same dialogue, Jesus continued, "All that the Father gives me will come to me, and whoever comes to me I will never drive away. . . . For my Father's will is that everyone who looks to the Son and believes in him shall have eternal life, and I will raise him up at the last day" (John 6:37, 40). God Himself is pursuing a love relationship with you. We pray you will respond to His call.

When you sense God is drawing you to Himself, what must you do to be saved? The Bible answers in a variety of ways. You've already read some of them. We've collected them for you in the margin. Below are some other ways the Bible describes what you must do to be saved.

> **10. Read the following scriptures, and underline the word or phrase that describes what a person must do to be saved. We've underlined the first one for you.**

> - "Yet to all who <u>received</u> him, to those <u>who believed in his name</u>, he gave the right to become children of God" (John 1:12).

> - "Everyone who believes in him receives forgiveness of sins through his name" (Acts 10:43).

> - "If you confess with your mouth, 'Jesus is Lord,' and believe in your heart that God raised him from the dead, you will be saved. For it is with your heart that you believe and are justified, and it is with your mouth that you confess and are saved. As the Scripture says, 'Anyone who trusts in him will never be put to shame.' For there is no difference between Jew and Gentile—the same Lord is Lord of all and richly blesses all who call on him, for, 'Everyone who calls on the name of the Lord will be saved'" (Rom. 10:9-13).

You may have underlined some additional words, but the summary of what we found is in the margin.

 **Read 2 Corinthians 6:1-2 in the lower-left margin. If you sense that now is, indeed, the time of God's favor and the day for your salvation, turn to Him in prayer. Just talk to Him in your own words. He will hear, understand, and respond to your prayer.**

- Agree with Him that you are a sinner and understand your need for a Savior.
- Tell Him of your belief and trust in Jesus' death and resurrection as the atoning sacrifice for your sins.
- Ask Him to forgive you for all your sins.
- Tell Him you want Jesus Christ to be Lord of your life and guide you in the right way of living.
- Ask Him in the name of Jesus Christ to save you and give you His Spirit.
- Thank Him now for saving you, and tell Him how much you love Him.
- Ask Him to help you begin growing from being a baby Christian to full maturity in Christ.

---

**"What must I do to be saved?"**

- "It is by grace you have been saved, through <u>faith</u>" (Eph. 2:8).
- "Whoever <u>believes</u> in the Son has eternal life" (John 3:36).
- "<u>Believe</u> in the Lord Jesus, and you will be saved—you and your household" (Acts 16:31).

**"What must I do to be saved?"**

- receive Him and believe in His name
- believe in Him
- confess (agree with God) that Jesus is Lord (Master, Ruler)
- believe God raised Christ from the dead
- trust in Him
- call on the name of the Lord (ask Him to forgive you and save you)

**2 Corinthians 6:1-2**

"As God's fellow workers we urge you not to receive God's grace in vain. For he says, 'In the time of my favor I heard you, and in the day of salvation I helped you.' I tell you, now is the time of God's favor, now is the day of salvation."

If you have prayed to receive Jesus as your Savior, let us be the first to welcome you to the family of God! The Bible says that the angels in heaven rejoice when a lost sinner comes to Christ (Luke 15:10). We rejoice with them.

When you trust Jesus as your Savior, God places the Holy Spirit in you to help you live like Christ. The Spirit will be your Teacher to help you understand Scripture. He will guide you in your prayer life. He will convict you of sin so you can turn away from it and stay in a right relationship with the Lord. Trust the Holy Spirit to help you grow more like Christ every day.

When you become a child of God, He wants to add you to a local church where you can be a part of the Body of Christ. These other believers will be able to help you follow the Lord. Because of God's Spirit in you, you'll also be able to help them become more like Christ. Look for the first opportunity to tell others of your decision and to begin to fellowship with other believers. We pray that your participation in a minichurch study of this course will be a wonderful beginning to your new life in Christ.

 **Conclude this part of the introduction by thanking God for what He has done for you through Jesus Christ. Ask Him how you can best share this message with others in your family.**

## PART 4: READING EPHESIANS 1–6

God's Word is very helpful in becoming the person God wants you to be (see 2 Tim. 3:16-17). To get the best overview of Ephesians, we want you to take time to read it through at a single sitting (15-30 minutes).

➤11. **Take time to read the entire Book of Ephesians (chapters 1–6). Place a check mark here when you have finished.** ❏

**2 Timothy 3:16-17**

"All Scripture is God-breathed and is useful for teaching, rebuking, correcting and training in righteousness, so that the man of God may be thoroughly equipped for every good work."

# INTRODUCTORY MINICHURCH MEETING

(Use the following suggestions under the guidance of your minichurch leader to prepare for your study of *Interacting with God in Ephesians 1–3*.)

## ARRIVAL ACTIVITIES

As members are arriving, complete the following:

❑ 1. Prepare a name tag. Print your first name in large letters so others can read it.

❑ 2. Prepare an information card for your leader. On the index card provided, write:
   • Name
   • Home mailing address
   • Home phone number
   • Work phone number (if you can receive calls)
   • E-mail address if you have one
   • Names and relationships of family members who live with you

❑ 3. If this is your first time to see the workbook, take a few minutes to flip through it and become familiar with its features.
   • Turn to the perforated cards in the back of the book and remove the bookmark in the upper-left corner. You can use it here to keep your place.
   • Write your name and phone number inside the front cover (just in case you misplace your book).
   • Read through the items on the contents page.
   • Read "Welcome" on page 4.
   • Turn to Lesson 1 on page 15, and notice that it's divided into four parts. Each is designed as a devotional study for one day. That way, you can complete your lesson study in four parts during the week.

❖ **Opening Prayer**

❖ **Singing Together**

Sing some favorite choruses and/or hymns.

## MINICHURCH LEADER'S OVERVIEW

Follow along as your leader reviews or introduces the following items:
   ❑ 1. Goals for the course (p. 5)
   ❑ 2. Self-paced Bible study features (pp. 5-6)
   ❑ 3. Minichurch meeting plans (p. 7)
   ❑ 4. Introduction assignments (Parts 2-4, pp. 8-13)
   ❑ 5. Glossary (p. 141)
   ❑ 6. Preparing for your minichurch meeting (p. 143)

❑ 7. Scripture memory cards (p. 145)
❑ 8. Bookmark features (p. 145)

❖ **Getting Acquainted**

Use the following to introduce yourself to the group:
   1. Name and family information.
   2. What city or town did you live in most while growing up?
   3. Where do you spend most of your working hours during the week (business, home, school, etc.)?
   4. What's one interesting fact about you that many people wouldn't know?
   5. Why did you decide to participate in this study?

❖ **Praying for One Another** (in fours or sixes)

Volunteers: Using the topics in Paul's prayer on your bookmark, spend a few minutes praying for your minichurch and for each other. Pray that God will help all of you to grow in a way that will bring Him glory.

❖ **Reading the Scriptures**

   1. Using volunteers, read each of the six chapters in Ephesians. Listen for one verse or idea in this reading that you would like to learn more about or that you would like to experience in a fresh way.
   2. Volunteers: State the verse or idea that you identified during the reading and the reason you chose it.

## GETTING READY FOR NEXT WEEK

As your leader describes the following items, make sure you understand what you need to do to be prepared for the next meeting:
   1. Next week's lesson assignment
   2. Time, place, and schedule of the weekly meetings
   3. Minichurch Meeting 1 plans (p. 24)

❖ **Questions and Answers**

Ask your leader any questions you have about the study.

❖ **Agreeing Together**

Turn to the Minichurch Covenant on page 144. Read and discuss the items in it. Make adjustments in the agreement if necessary. Pray together, asking God to bless your relationships during this study. Then date your book and take turns signing one another's books.

❖ **Closing Prayer**

❖ **Optional: "Breaking Bread" Together**

# Lesson 1
# Looking Up

**"Switzerland of the New Testament"**

I (Gene) remember the first time I stepped out the front door of the boardinghouse where my wife and I were staying in Innsbruck, Austria. After ministering in Eastern Europe, we were spending a few days relaxing in this onetime location of the Winter Olympics.

I looked up to behold one of the most spectacular sights I've ever seen. Rising from the valley floor was a range of mountains that nearly took my breath away. Though I love the Colorado Rockies, this view of the Alps was far grander than anything I had seen before.

All mountains are created by God and are beautiful and spectacular in their own right. But some stand out above others. Just so, we also know that "all Scripture is God-breathed and is useful for teaching, rebuking, correcting and training in righteousness" (2 Tim. 3:16). But Ephesians stands out as one of the Holy Spirit's most lofty products of inspiration. Viewed and understood correctly, it is spiritually breathtaking. In a relatively small section of the Bible, Paul takes us from earth to heaven as he unveils a Christian's wonderful and marvelous spiritual blessings in Christ. Thus, someone has called this letter "the Switzerland of the New Testament."

*If God has His way during this study, we will all be forever changed for His glory!*

We (Gene and Claude) consider this opportunity a great privilege. We get to be your personal "tour guides" as we study this grand message together. If God has His way during this study, we will all be forever changed for His glory!

We all have times in our lives when we feel down. They may be brief periods, or they may last for days or even weeks. These down periods occur for a variety of reasons. The cause may be physical: We're tired. The demands of life may have left us exhausted. The cause may be psychological: Stress has taken its toll. Or perhaps we're facing a natural result of a prolonged emotionally high experience. The cause may also be spiritual: Perhaps we're living out of the will of God. Sin and guilt may have gripped our minds and hearts. Or we may have taken our eyes off God and focused on the circumstances of life around us.

Whatever the cause, there's a foundational solution. We must look beyond ourselves to the God who cares about us and loves us unconditionally—no matter what the source of our depression.

- If you're physically exhausted, you need rest.
- If you're psychologically drained, you need relief from the pressure and a friend with an understanding and listening ear.
- If you're living only for yourself, you need to focus on God and others.
- In some instances, you may need professional counseling or medical help.
- But in *all* circumstances, you need to look up.

*So if you're feeling down, look up!*

God the Father and Jesus our Savior care more than any other person—pastor, doctor, or counselor. One of Paul's themes in Ephesians 1–3 focuses on a Christian's hope. So if you're feeling down, let Paul help you look up. Read and study this letter to the Ephesian Christians, and be renewed and strengthened by a fresh understanding of your wonderful position in Jesus Christ.

## PART 1: INTERACTING WITH THE SCRIPTURE

### Reading / Hearing God's Word

**Read or Listen to:**
❑ Ephesians 1–6
❑ Ephesians 1–3
❑ Ephesians 1:1-23

**➤1.** Select one of the reading (or listening) options in the margin. Using your Bible, read or listen to the passage of Scripture. As you begin, ask God to speak to you through His Word. Watch for one verse or idea that's especially meaningful to you today. Once you finish reading, check the box indicating the passage you read.

### Meditating on God's Word

**Meaningful Verse or Idea**

_____

_____

_____

**➤2.** In the margin, write a brief summary of the meaningful verse or idea you just identified.

### Memorizing God's Word

**Most Meaningful Passage**

_____

**➤3.** Turn to the perforated Scripture memory cards at the back of your workbook. Read through the 12 passages we have selected for memorization. Select one of the passages that's the most meaningful to you, and write the reference in the margin.

**➤4.** Now decide on how many scriptures you will memorize during the coming 12 weeks. Check your choice. One scripture:

❑ each week    ❑ every other week    ❑ each month

**➤5.** Select and tear out a Scripture memory card from the back of your book. Use the tips for memorizing Scripture on your bookmark. If this is your first time to memorize Scripture, spend a little extra time working on memorizing this first passage. If you haven't already done so, remove your bookmark from the perforated card sheet and place it here in your workbook. One side has the tips for memorizing scripture.

### Understanding God's Word

**Ephesians 1:1-2**

"Paul, an apostle of Christ Jesus by the will of God,

"To the saints in Ephesus, the faithful in Christ Jesus:

"Grace and peace to you from God our Father and the Lord Jesus Christ."

**➤6.** Read again the focal passage for this week's lesson (Eph. 1:1-2) in the margin. Underline any key phrases or ideas that seem especially meaningful to you. Then read the brief definitions of key words below. This will prepare you for the remainder of our study this week.

- ♦ **apostle:** a delegate, messenger, one that is sent, an ambassador of the gospel, a commissioner of Christ.
- ♦ **Christ:** the Messiah, the anointed One.
- ♦ **Jesus:** personal name meaning "Jehovah saves."
- ♦ **will:** a determination, choice, purpose, desire, inclination, pleasure.
- ♦ **saints:** sacred ones, ones set apart as holy, set apart for God, consecrated.
- ♦ **faithful:** trustworthy, trustful, believing, sure, true.
- ♦ **grace:** graciousness, acceptable, benefit, favor, gift.
- ♦ **peace:** prosperity, quietness, rest, set at one, whole.
- ♦ **Lord:** supreme in authority, controller, Master.

**➤7.** Look back through this list of words. Circle one that you would like to understand or experience more fully.

### Looking through the Scripture to God

 Now pause to pray. Thank God for giving us the Bible so we can come to know Him. Ask Him to be your Teacher during this study. Give Him permission to use His Word to speak to you in any way He chooses.

## PART 2: INTRODUCTION TO EPHESIANS

**Ephesians 1:1**

"Paul, an apostle of Christ Jesus by the will of God . . ."

**Paul—the Author.** The Book of Ephesians is a letter written by a man named Paul (Eph. 1:1). His original name was Saul of Tarsus, and he first appeared in the biblical record after the church was founded at Jerusalem. Christians already numbered in the thousands. The scene was dramatic and chilling. Stephen had just delivered a powerful witness before the Sanhedrin, a group of unbelieving Jews who were the primary leaders in Israel. His message was so penetrating and spiritually convicting that they responded with threats and anger. "They were furious"—so much so that they "gnashed their teeth at him" (Acts 7:54). Their next move was to rush him, drag him out of the city, and stone him. And as they did, they "laid their clothes at the feet of a young man named Saul" who "was there, giving approval to his death" (Acts 7:58; 8:1).

➤ **8. When did this Paul (Saul) first appear in the Bible? Check one.**
❑ a. In the Old Testament before Christ.
❑ b. During the life and ministry of Jesus Christ.
❑ c. After the establishment of the first church in Jerusalem.

From that day forward, Paul (Saul) led the persecution against Christians. His goal was to "destroy the church." Consequently, he went "from house to house" and "dragged off men and women and put them in prison" (Acts 8:3). This angry young man was so intense and successful in his efforts that Christians could no longer stay in Jerusalem. They were scattered throughout the New Testament world (Acts 8:1). But Paul wasn't satisfied. He got permission from the high priest to go to Damascus to carry on his same murderous activities (Acts 9:1-2). And then it happened! "As he neared Damascus on his journey, suddenly a light from heaven flashed around him. He fell to the ground and heard a voice say to him, 'Saul, Saul, why do you persecute me?'" (Acts 9:3-4). The voice was that of Jesus Christ. Paul became a believer then and there.

**Acts 8:1**

"On that day a great persecution broke out against the church at Jerusalem, and all except the apostles were scattered throughout Judea and Samaria."

**Acts 9:1-2**

"Saul was still breathing out murderous threats against the Lord's disciples. He went to the high priest and asked him for letters to the synagogues in Damascus, so that if he found any there who belonged to the Way, whether men or women, he might take them as prisoners to Jerusalem."

In Damascus, God revealed to Paul that he was God's chosen instrument to carry the message of Jesus Christ in a special way to the Gentile (non-Jewish) world (Acts 9:15). Paul later went on three missionary tours, leading people to Jesus Christ and starting churches. The church at Ephesus was one of these (Acts 19). Paul is the one who wrote this letter. He also is responsible for 12 other letters that have been included in the New Testament.

♦ **apostle:** a delegate, messenger, one that is sent, an ambassador of the Gospel, a commisioner of Christ.

As in most of his letters, Paul identified himself as an apostle. He later described his special calling in Christ as an apostle to the Gentiles (Eph. 3:1-13). An apostle is one who serves as a messenger or ambassador of another. Few individuals were identified as apostles other than the original 12 disciples; only Paul was ranked with those Jesus personally called and appointed to launch the church. He, too, had a direct encounter with Jesus Christ.

**1 Corinthians 12:28, 31**

"In the church God has appointed first of all apostles. . . . But eagerly desire the greater gifts."

**Ephesians 2:20**

". . . built on the foundation of the apostles and prophets, with Christ Jesus himself as the chief cornerstone."

An apostle was no ordinary person in the New Testament church. Apostles were among the "greater gifts" to the Body of Christ (1 Cor. 12:28, 31). Later in Ephesians, Paul described apostleship along with prophetic ability as being foundational gifts (Eph. 2:20). Don't misunderstand. Paul was not expressing arrogance. He stated, "For I am the least of the apostles and do not even deserve to be called an apostle, because I persecuted the church of God. But," he continued, "by the grace of God I am what I am" (1 Cor. 15:9-10).

➤9. Write the name of the author of Ephesians, and describe two facts you know about his life.

_____

_____

**Acts 28:30**

"For two whole years Paul stayed there in his own rented house and welcomed all who came to see him."

**Time and Place of Writing.** We know from Ephesians 3:1 and 4:1 that Paul was "a prisoner for the Lord." Most likely Paul wrote this letter from a Roman prison around A.D. 60 or 61. It's classified as one of the prison epistles, along with Philemon, Philippians, and Colossians. Though Paul was under custody in Rome, Luke reported that he was able to have his own rented home where he could freely receive visitors (Acts 28:30). Though in prison, he had more time to think, reflect, pray, and write than when he was actively involved on his missionary tours. Perhaps this is one reason the letter is so outstanding. In this semiprivate location, he had more time to spend in quiet fellowship with the Holy Spirit.

➤10. When and from where did Paul write this letter?

_____

**Ephesians 1:1**

"Paul, . . . to the saints in Ephesus, the faithful in Christ Jesus."

**To the Saints.** Some Bible interpreters believe this letter to the Ephesians was designed by Paul to be a letter that circulated from church to church. Thus, Paul addressed this letter "to the saints." This conclusion is based on several facts. First, the earliest New Testament manuscripts do not include the words "in Ephesus." Second, Paul omitted any personal greeting in the letter even though he had spent much time in Ephesus and had close friends there. In each of his other letters, he included personal greetings. Third, the letter treats a broad spectrum of teaching that does not relate to specific aspects of a particular local church. In fact, it's one of the few letters in which Paul dealt extensively with the concept of the universal church (that Body which includes all believers in Jesus Christ). For these reasons, many believe this letter was a doctrinal tract for the churches throughout Asia. At some point in the circulation of the letter, a copy came to Ephesus. This is the letter that became known to the early church.

➤11. If you were to read a letter addressed "to the saints," would you consider yourself to be included? Check your response.
   ❑ a. No, saints are super-godly people who can perform miracles.
   ❑ b. Yes, saints are all those who have received God's salvation.

♦ **saints:** sacred ones, ones set apart as holy, set apart for God, consecrated.

♦ **faithful:** trustworthy, trustful, believing, sure, true.

Though some groups have a specific and measurable definition of *saint*, Paul was addressing all believers in Jesus Christ in the churches. These are ones who have been set apart for God. They are holy—not because of their own good deeds but because they belong to God, who is holy. Paul called them "the faithful in Christ Jesus." They had placed their faith and trust in Jesus Christ, and they were seeking to remain loyal to Him.

➤12. To whom did Paul write this letter? Check all that apply.
   ❑ a. a few very godly Christians
   ❑ b. people who were set apart for God
   ❑ c. believers in the gods of Rome
   ❑ d. believers in Jesus Christ
   ❑ e. Christian churches in Asia
   ❑ f. the church at Jerusalem

🙏 Pause to thank God for providing such a special letter for His saints. Ask Him for help in remaining faithful to Him during this study.

**Ephesians 1:2**

"Grace and peace to you from God our Father and the Lord Jesus Christ."

**The Christian Life**

1. Past—Regeneration
2. Present—Sanctification
3. Future—Glorification

## GLORIFICATION

**1 Corinthians 15:51-52**

"We will all be changed—in a flash, in the twinkling of an eye, at the last trumpet. For the trumpet will sound, the dead will be raised imperishable, and we will be changed."

**Philippians 3:20-21**

"Our citizenship is in heaven. And we eagerly await a Savior from there, the Lord Jesus Christ, who . . . will transform our lowly bodies so that <u>they will be like his glorious body</u>."

**2 Thessalonians 1:10**

". . . on the day he [the Lord] comes to be glorified in his holy people and to be marveled at among all those who have believed. This includes you, because you believed our testimony to you."

**1 John 3:2**

"Now we are children of God, and what we will be has not yet been made known. But we know that when he appears, we shall be like him."

♦ **grace:** graciousness, acceptable, benefit, favor, gift.

### PART 3: GRACE AND PEACE TO YOU

Paul the apostle wrote a circular letter to the churches in Asia, including the church at Ephesus. He wrote to the saints—all in the churches who had turned by faith to Jesus Christ and been saved. Next, Paul greeted the readers in a way that would have been common in a letter of that day. He expressed his desire that the readers would receive grace and peace from "God our Father and the Lord Jesus Christ" (Eph. 1:2). To better understand what he wanted them to receive, we need to review the nature of the Christian life.

**The Christian Life in Three Parts.** In the introduction (pp. 8-13), we describe how, when a person turns to Christ in faith, he is saved or "born again." That's a one-time experience. We call it "regeneration." God replaces your sinful nature with a new nature. You are given a new life in Christ. This is the past part of the Christian life. But there are two more parts.

As we described in a previous part of this lesson, when you are saved you become a "saint"—one set apart (or sanctified) for God and made holy. God places His Spirit in you and begins the process of conforming you to the image of Christ Himself. This is a lifelong process. It's the present part of salvation and can be called "progressive sanctification." More and more you are set apart from your old way of life and your old nature. You're progressively (in stages) becoming more like Christ and more fully surrendered to the leadership of the Holy Spirit. You're turning from old patterns of thinking and living to a new way of life.

▶13. **Match the part of the Christian life on the left with the correct title on the right. Draw a line from the number to the correct letter.**

1. Past                   a. Glorification
2. Present                b. Regeneration
3. Future                 c. Sanctification

Regeneration describes the past part of your Christian life (1-b). Sanctification describes the present process you are going through (2-c). The day will come when you will be glorified and become like Jesus Christ more completely than ever. That's the future part of your Christian life (3-a).

▶14. **Read through the Scriptures under "Glorification" in the margin, and underline the words or phrases that describe what will take place in the future for the Christian. We've underlined one for you.**

▶15. **What is the future part of the Christian life called?**

_____

In the future, we will become like Jesus. We will be changed. We will be given a new and glorious body. Jesus Christ Himself will be glorified in us. What a day that will be!

**Grace to You.** Paul began his letter to the saints by saying "grace . . . to you" (Eph. 1:2). What did he mean? Grace is God's favor and blessing that He gives to us freely. We're going to study this topic in much more detail in Lesson 8: "Experiencing God's Grace." In that lesson we'll focus on God's saving grace, the free gift of salvation He gives when we place our faith in Him.

Paul had experienced this saving grace. He never got over the grace that God extended to him that day on the Damascus road. The Lord could have struck him dead instead of blind. Paul knew he deserved eternal separation from God. He had taken the lives of some of God's chosen people. Thus he wrote to Timothy, "Even though

I was once a blasphemer and a persecutor and a violent man, I was shown mercy because I acted in ignorance and unbelief. The grace of our Lord was poured out on me abundantly, along with the faith and love that are in Christ Jesus" (1 Tim. 1:13-14).

The apostle Paul knew by experience that God saves sinners. He classified himself as the "worst." But he also said, "For that very reason I was shown mercy so that in me, the worst of sinners, Christ Jesus might display his unlimited patience as an example for those who would believe on him and receive eternal life" (1 Tim. 1:16). In other words, Paul knew that if God could save him, He could save anybody! Paul never forgot that reality. It was indelibly impressed upon his heart and affected the rest of his life.

**►16. Describe in your own words what God's saving grace is.**

_____

_____

When Paul wished grace for his readers, they had already experienced God's saving grace. But another aspect of His amazing grace is the continuing and sustaining grace He gives us in the present. We need it for our sanctification. Apart from His favor and freely given help, we could never change our lives to be like Jesus. We could never experience daily victory over sin and temptation. Paul experienced this sustaining grace:

> "To keep me from becoming conceited because of these surpassingly great revelations, there was given me a thorn in my flesh, a messenger of Satan, to torment me. Three times I pleaded with the Lord to take it away from me. But he said to me, 'My grace is sufficient for you, for my power is made perfect in weakness.' Therefore I will boast all the more gladly about my weaknesses, so that Christ's power may rest on me. That is why, for Christ's sake, I delight in weaknesses, in insults, in hardships, in persecutions, in difficulties. For when I am weak, then I am strong" (2 Cor. 12:7-10).

The writer of Hebrews tells how this grace is available:

> "We do not have a high priest who is unable to sympathize with our weaknesses, but we have one who has been tempted in every way, just as we are—yet was without sin. Let us then approach the throne of grace with confidence, so that we may receive mercy and find grace to help us in our time of need" (Heb. 4:15-16).

This continuing and sustaining grace is available to help us in times of weakness and need. It's available to help us be victorious over sin and temptation. It's available in abundance to enable us to do good works out of our love for the Lord (2 Cor. 9:8). Even once we have received God's grace in salvation, we need His continuing favor and blessing—His grace—for daily living. This is the grace Paul desired for all the saints to whom he was writing. We pray that God would grant you this continuing and sustaining grace.

 Take some time to pray for God to give you sustaining grace. Jesus, your High Priest, knows every way you need this grace. He was tempted just like you. Approach God's throne with confidence, and ask for mercy and grace to help in your times of weakness and need.

- Ask God for grace to help you in times of temptation.
- Ask God for grace to sustain you through times of suffering.
- Ask God for grace to live victoriously over sin.

**Paul knew that if God could save him, He could save anybody!**

**2 Corinthians 9:8**
"God is able to make all <u>grace</u> abound to you, so that in all things at all times, having all that you need, you will abound in every good work."

• Ask God for abounding grace that will enable you in every good work.

• Thank God for the saving grace He already has given you.

• Thank God for the sustaining grace He gives you daily.

◆ **peace:** prosperity, quietness, rest, set at one, whole.

**Romans 5:1**

"Since we have been justified through faith, we have peace with God through our Lord Jesus Christ."

**Peace to You.** Paul wanted his readers to experience God's grace and peace. There's a peace with God that comes when you're saved and justified—placed in a forgiven relationship with Him (Rom. 5:1). You're no longer the object of His wrath. You're at peace with Him. Again, this is a past and continuing experience of peace with God for the Christian.

Paul's readers had already experienced this kind of peace. So what did he desire for them? The Greek word for peace is related to the Hebrew greeting "Shalom." This peace is not just the absence of trouble or conflict. It's far more positive. It's a wish for prosperity, rest, and wholeness. In fact, this kind of peace can be experienced in the middle of problems and difficulties. It's like the eye of a hurricane—peace and calmness with a storm all around.

**Lacking Peace?**

• at home with spouse, children

• at work with boss, coworkers

• with parents or relatives

• financial problems

• health concerns

• community safety concerns

• at church with other believers

• with neighbors, friends

➤**17. Before we look to the Bible for greater understanding, think about the areas of your life where you need peace. Using the list in the margin to prompt your thinking, make a list below of areas or relationships where peace is lacking in your life.**

_____

_____

_____

 **18. As you read the following scriptures, pause and ask God to guide you into the peace only He can give in the circumstances listed above. Ask Him what you may need to do to receive or experience the peace He desires for you.**

• "Do not be anxious about anything, but in everything, by prayer and petition, with thanksgiving, present your requests to God. And the peace of God, which transcends all understanding, will guard your hearts and your minds in Christ Jesus" (Phil. 4:6-7).

• "Let the peace of Christ rule in your hearts, since as members of one body you were called to peace" (Col. 3:15).

• "May God himself, the God of peace, sanctify you through and through. May your whole spirit, soul and body be kept blameless at the coming of our Lord Jesus Christ. The one who calls you is faithful and he will do it" (1 Thess. 5:23-24).

• "Now may the Lord of peace himself give you peace at all times and in every way. The Lord be with all of you" (2 Thess. 3:16).

• "Peace I leave with you; my peace I give you. I do not give to you as the world gives. Do not let your hearts be troubled and do not be afraid" (John 14:27).

• "I have told you these things, so that in me you may have peace. In this world you will have trouble. But take heart! I have overcome the world" (John 16:33).

• "The mind of sinful man is death, but the mind controlled by the Spirit is life and peace" (Rom. 8:6).

• "May the God of hope fill you with all joy and peace as you trust in him, so that you may overflow with hope by the power of the Holy Spirit" (Rom. 15:13).

## PART 4: GLORY IN THE CHURCH

Paul's letter to the Ephesians (and all the saints and churches to which it circulated) was written to help them become all God wanted them to be. This was not just for the sake of the churches, although they certainly would benefit. The greater purpose was for God to get glory through the church. In the following lessons, we will be looking at some of the ways God gets glory through a new and changed people.

As we begin this study of *Interacting with God in Ephesians 1–3* with you, we have the same hope. We pray that God will use this study of Paul's letter to get glory. In these three chapters of Ephesians, Paul prayed a great prayer for the believers. We want you to begin praying this prayer for yourself and your minichurch.

➤19. You should already have a bookmark that you have removed from the back of your workbook. One side has the tips for memorizing Scripture. The other side has Paul's prayer for the church outlined for you to use as you pray each week. If you don't already have the bookmark in your hand, turn to the back of your workbook and remove the perforated bookmark at the upper-left corner. Turn to the side that has Paul's prayer.

At the end of Paul's prayer in Ephesians 3:20-21, he described his desire for God to receive glory through the church and in Jesus Christ.

➤20. Read Ephesians 3:20-21 below, and write how much God is able to do to reveal His glory in the church and in Christ.

> **Ephesians 3:20-21**—"Now to him who is able to do immeasurably more than all we ask or imagine, according to his power that is at work within us, to him be glory in the church and in Christ Jesus throughout all generations, for ever and ever! Amen."

_____

_____

Prayer is a powerful relationship with the God who can do "immeasurably more than all we ask or imagine." When He does this in the church, it reveals His glory to us and to others who observe what He has done. We want you to begin praying that God will do this "much more" in your life, in your family, in your minichurch, and in your church as a whole. We also pray that this "much more" will be done in all the Body of Christ in your city and ultimately around the world for His glory.

My Minichurch Members

_____

_____

_____

_____

_____

_____

_____

_____

_____

_____

➤21. Spend the remainder of this lesson praying Paul's prayer for yourself and the members of your minichurch. Begin by listing the names of your minichurch members (or as many as you know) in the left margin.

 Now spend time with each of Paul's requests. We'll study more about their meaning in future lessons. For now, trust the Holy Spirit to guide your praying according to God's will. Pray about each request, and make it personal and specific as you pray for yourself and for those whose names you've written in the margin.

**Ephesians 1:17-19**—"I keep asking that the God of our Lord Jesus Christ, the glorious Father,

- may give you the Spirit of wisdom and revelation, so that you may know him better.

- I pray also that the eyes of your heart may be enlightened

- in order that you may know

    – the hope to which he has called you,

    – the riches of his glorious inheritance in the saints, and

    – his incomparably great power for us who believe."

**Ephesians 3:16-19**—"I pray that out of his glorious riches he may

- strengthen you with power through his Spirit in your inner being,

- so that Christ may dwell in your hearts through faith.

- And I pray that you, being rooted and established in love,

- may have power, together with all the saints, to grasp how wide and long and high and deep is the love of Christ, and

- to know this love that surpasses knowledge—

- that you may be filled to the measure of all the fullness of God."

— **Amen!**

# MINICHURCH MEETING 1

## BEFORE THE MEETING

❑ 1. Turn to "Preparing for Your Minichurch Meeting" on page 143. Use it as a guide to get ready for this meeting. Check the box above after you have prepared.

❑ 2. Unless God should direct otherwise, your minichurch leader will be using the following outline to guide your meeting. You may want to look over the questions and activities so you will be better prepared to participate.

## DURING THE MEETING

❖ **Opening Prayer**

❖ **Singing Together**

Consider singing "Amazing Grace" and "I've Got Peace Like a River" together with other choruses and hymns.

❖ **Building Relationships**

Give opportunity for members to talk about one of the following:

1. Describe a time when you experienced a "mountaintop" encounter with God—a time when you knew God's presence or activity in a way that took you to a spiritual high point in your life.

2. Describe a time in your life when you were at a low point physically, emotionally, or spiritually and you encountered God as He comforted, encouraged, strengthened, or revived you.

❖ **Responding to God in Prayer**

Volunteers: Lead the group in praising and thanking God for the ways He cares for His children. If testimonies of experiencing God are few, pray that God would use the days ahead to minister to your individual, family, and church needs in a way that will bring glory to Him.

❖ **Interacting with the Scriptures** (in fours or sixes)

1. What verse or passage of Scripture has been most meaningful or challenging to you this week? How has God used it to speak to you? What significant actions have you taken this week because of something God revealed through His Word?

2. (p. 16, #4) What are your Scripture memory plans for this course?

3. (p. 16) Volunteers: Recite the memory verse you learned this week and/or explain any special meaning you gained from it. If this is your first time, you have permission to use your Scripture cards to aid your memory.

4. (p. 16, #7) What word or phrase from Ephesians 1:1-2 have you come to better understand or experience this week? Describe your understanding or experience.

❖ **Reviewing the Lesson**

1. (p. 18, #9) What do you know about Paul, the author of Ephesians? Let different members state facts about his life and ministry.

2. (p. 18) When and where did Paul write this letter? What do you think he may have been thinking about his past ministry and his future?

3. (p. 18, #12) To whom did Paul write this letter? Who is a "saint"?

4. (p. 19) What are three parts of the Christian life? Briefly describe each one.

❖ **Applying the Truths to Life**

1. As you read Parts 2 and 3 in the introduction about salvation, what was particularly meaningful or helpful? Can you think of people who need to know and understand that message? What are some ways you might use to present that message to others?

2. What kind of grace did Paul want these saints to experience? In what ways do Christians need God's sustaining grace?

3. What is the peace Paul desired for the saints? In what kinds of circumstances do Christians need to experience God's peace?

4. (In fours or sixes, p. 21) Volunteers or all: Explain ways you (as an individual) need to experience God's grace and peace in your life, family, work, or church.

❖ **Praying for One Another** (in fours or sixes)

After everyone in your smaller group has had a chance to state needs for grace and peace, pray specifically for one another. Make sure every individual in the group gets prayed for. If someone is dealing with a major concern, spend extra time praying for that one.

❖ **Ministering to One Another**

What needs (if any) of your minichurch members have you become aware of during this meeting (or this week) that the Body may need to care for? What can we do to meet the needs or to help connect the person with those who can help? Are there things we need to do today or this week to help?

❖ **Reaching Out to Others**

Are there people in your circles of influence who need a saving relationship with Jesus Christ and for whom God seems to be giving you a special burden? What can we pray or do to help you carry that burden? Are there individuals you want to invite to participate in this study?

❖ **Closing Prayer**

❖ **Optional: "Breaking Bread" Together**

# LESSON 2
# LOOKING UP TO GOD THE FATHER

**God in Space**

Man's first explorations of outer space led to some interesting comments about the existence of God. For example, as soon as Russia's first satellite entered space, the Moscow magazine *Krokidil* indicated that "creation, from a communist point of view, is at last under new management." Later, after his return from space, a Russian astronaut said,

> "Some people say there is a God out there . . . . But in my travels around the earth all day long, I looked around and didn't see Him . . . . I saw no God or angels. The rocket was made by our own people. I don't believe in God. I believe in man, his strength, his possibilities, his reason."

By contrast, astronaut John Glenn on one occasion delivered a sermon entitled "Why I Know There Is a God." In simple terms, he described his belief in God and in Christian principles. He concluded with the thought that man is placed on earth as a free agent. He is given freedom of choice. Only he can decide whether he will or won't live by the guidelines Christ followed and taught.

On another occasion, astronaut James McDivitt (who orbited the earth 62 times aboard *Gemini IV*) said,

> "I did not see God looking into my space-cabin window, as I do not see God looking into my car's windshield on earth. But I could recognize His work in the stars as well as when walking among flowers in a garden. If you can be with God on earth, you can be with God in space as well."

**Psalm 8:1, 3-4, 9**

"O LORD, our Lord, how majestic is your name in all the earth! You have set your glory above the heavens. . . .

"When I consider your heavens, the work of your fingers, the moon and the stars, which you have set in place, what is man that you are mindful of him, and the son of man that you care for him? . . .

"O LORD, our Lord, how majestic is your name in all the earth!"

King David put all these thoughts in proper perspective when he said, "The fool says in his heart, 'There is no God'" (Ps. 14:1). Why is this true? Again David spoke clearly: "The heavens declare the glory of God; the skies proclaim the work of his hands" (Ps. 19:1). Another psalmist personalized David's words. He knew where to look for guidance and encouragement, particularly in a time of deep need. Thus he wrote, "I lift up my eyes to the hills—where does my help come from? My help comes from the LORD, the Maker of heaven and earth" (Ps. 121:1-2).

**Take a moment to turn your heart to the God of creation. Think about the beauty of the earth. Think about the vastness and glory of the heavens. Wonder at the fact that the God of all creation knows and cares about you. Then pray to the Lord the text of Psalm 8 in the margin.**

In Ephesians, Paul helps every Christian focus on God as the source of all blessing, grace, and power. As you study this lesson, lift up your eyes, your mind, and your heart, and focus your attention on God—your heavenly Father. Watch for opportunities for your mind and heart to be drawn to praise Him for what He has done.

## PART 1: INTERACTING WITH THE SCRIPTURE

### Reading / Hearing God's Word

➤1. Select one of the reading (or listening) options in the margin. Using your Bible, read or listen to the passage of Scripture. As you begin, ask God to speak to you through His Word. Watch for one verse or idea that is especially meaningful to you today. Once you finish reading, check the box indicating the passage you read.

### Meditating on God's Word

➤2. In the margin, write a brief summary of the meaningful verse or idea you just identified.

### Memorizing God's Word

➤3. Select and tear out a new Scripture memory card from the back of your book, or continue reviewing the one you started with last week. For a new verse, use the tips for memorizing Scripture on your bookmark.

### Understanding God's Word

➤4. Read again the focal passage for this week's lesson (Eph. 1:3-6) in the margin. Underline any key phrases or ideas that seem especially meaningful to you. Then read the brief definitions of key words below. This will prepare you for the remainder of this week's study.

- ♦ **blessed:** invoke a benediction upon, bless, praise, cause to prosper or make happy.
- ♦ **blessings:** benefits.
- ♦ **spiritual:** not carnal, of the spirit as opposed to the flesh.
- ♦ **chosen:** selected as a kindness or favor.
- ♦ **holy:** sacred, pure, blameless, consecrated.
- ♦ **blameless:** without blame, unblemished, faultless, unblameable.
- ♦ **love:** [*agape*] godly affection, benevolence, seeking the very best for another.
- ♦ **predestined:** to limit or set out in advance, determine before, ordain.
- ♦ **adopted:** placed in position as a son (child).
- ♦ **praise:** laudation, commendation, a commendable thing.
- ♦ **glorious/glory:** splendor, honor, the evidence of God's wonderful work or character.
- ♦ **grace:** graciousness, the divine influence upon the heart, and its reflection in the life, acceptable, benefit, favor, gift.

➤5. Look back through this list of words. Circle one that you would like to understand or experience more fully.

### Looking through the Scripture to God

 **Now pause to pray.**
- Thank God for what He has done for you.
- Express to Him your praise and worship.
- Ask Him to enable you to be holy and blameless in your daily living so you can bring glory to Him.
- Talk to Him about anything the Scriptures have brought to mind.
- Close by praying Ephesians 1:17-19 and 3:16-19 (on your bookmark) for yourself and your minichurch.

---

**Read or Listen to:**

❏ Ephesians 1–6
❏ Ephesians 1–3
❏ Ephesians 1:1-23

**Meaningful Verse or Idea**

_____

_____

_____

**Ephesians 1:3-6**
"Praise be to the God and Father of our Lord Jesus Christ, who has blessed us in the heavenly realms with every spiritual blessing in Christ. For he chose us in him before the creation of the world to be holy and blameless in his sight. In love he predestined us to be adopted as his sons through Jesus Christ, in accordance with his pleasure and will—to the praise of his glorious grace, which he has freely given us in the One he loves."

### PART 2: COUNT YOUR BLESSINGS

Paul began this letter to Christians by extending "grace and peace . . . from God the Father and the Lord Jesus Christ" (Eph. 1:2). Then he launched into a grand statement of praise and adoration. During the next three lessons, we're going to study this hymn of praise to better understand all God has done for us. The hymn has three natural divisions:

**Hymn Divisions**

1. God the Father (vv. 3-6)—the Scripture focus for this week's lesson

2. God the Son (vv. 7-12)—the Scripture focus for Lesson 3

3. God the Holy Spirit (vv. 13-14)—the Scripture focus for Lesson 4

Paul concluded each division with a similar refrain, much as the hymns we sing often have a refrain at the end of each verse.

➤ 6. **After you read the three statements of the refrain below, go back and circle the two main ideas or words that they all have in common.**

**Hymn Refrain**

1. "to the praise of his glorious grace, which he has freely given us in the One he loves" (1:6)

2. "in order that we, who were the first to hope in Christ, might be for the praise of his glory" (1:12)

3. "who is a deposit guaranteeing our inheritance until the redemption of those who are God's possession—to the praise of his glory" (1:14).

Did you circle *praise* and *glory* (or *glorious*)? Paul told us that all of God's spiritual blessings for us are designed to bring praise to Him. They reveal His glory in the wonderful work He has done in us. All that Paul taught is related to God's plan of salvation for lost humanity.

**God's Work of Salvation**

1. God the Father planned it.

2. God the Son—Jesus Christ—carried out the plan.

3. God the Spirit—the Holy Spirit—has guaranteed that the plan will be fulfilled.

In this paragraph, one thing is clear: God is all in all. He has blessed us with every spiritual blessing! In Lessons 2–4, we're going to look more carefully at the spiritual blessings God has given to those who have surrendered their lives to Him as Savior and Lord.

➤ 7. **As you read the following scriptures, underline the words or phrases that describe the things God has done for you—the ways He has blessed you. We have underlined one for you.**

**God the Father Planned Your Salvation** (Eph. 1:3-6)

> "Praise be to the God and Father of our Lord Jesus Christ, who has blessed us in the heavenly realms with every spiritual blessing in Christ. For <u>he chose us</u> in him before the creation of the world to be holy and blameless in his sight. In love he predestined us to be adopted as his sons through Jesus Christ, in accordance with his pleasure and will—to the praise of his glorious grace, which he has freely given us in the One he loves."

**God the Son Carried Out the Plan** (Eph. 1:7-12)

"In him we have redemption through his blood, the forgiveness of sins, in accordance with the riches of God's grace that he lavished on us with all wisdom and understanding. And he made known to us the mystery of his will according to his good pleasure, which he purposed in Christ, to be put into effect when the times will have reached their fulfillment—to bring all things in heaven and on earth together under one head, even Christ.

"In him we were also chosen, having been predestined according to the plan of him who works out everything in conformity with the purpose of his will, in order that we, who were the first to hope in Christ, might be for the praise of his glory."

**God the Spirit Is Your Guarantee** (Eph. 1:13-14)

"And you also were included in Christ when you heard the word of truth, the gospel of your salvation. Having believed, you were marked in him with a seal, the promised Holy Spirit, who is a deposit guaranteeing our inheritance until the redemption of those who are God's possession—to the praise of his glory."

Hasn't God blessed us in wonderful ways? As you read this list of blessings, however, you may have realized you are not experiencing the joy of your blessed relationship to God. That's why we're going to spend three lessons studying God's spiritual blessings. You can look up to God when you're feeling down. You can focus on your blessings rather than your problems. In the margin, we've listed some of the blessings you could have underlined. You may have underlined others as well.

An old hymn encourages you to take time to count your blessings no matter what your circumstances—good or bad.

➤ **8. As you read the hymn below, underline the times when you can and should count your blessings. We've underlined one for you.**

## COUNT YOUR BLESSINGS

by Johnson Oatman Jr.

When upon life's billows you are tempest-tossed,
<u>When you are discouraged</u>, thinking all is lost,
Count your many blessings, name them one by one,
And it will surprise you what the Lord hath done.

Are you ever burdened with a load of care?
Does the cross seem heavy you are called to bear?
Count your many blessings, every doubt will fly,
And you will keep singing as the days go by.

When you look at others with their lands and gold,
Think that Christ has promised you his wealth untold;
Count your many blessings, wealth can never buy
Your reward in heaven, nor your home on high.

So, amid the conflict, whether great or small,
Do not be disheartened—God is over all;
Count your many blessings, angels will attend,
Help and comfort give you to your journey's end.

(continued)

---

### OUR SPIRITUAL BLESSINGS

**Part 1**

• He chose us.

• He predestined us to be adopted as His children.

• He has freely given us His grace.

**Part 2**

• He redeemed us.

• He provided forgiveness for our sins.

• He lavished grace on us with all wisdom and understanding.

• He made known to us the mystery of His will.

**Part 3**

• He included us in Christ.

• He marked us in Christ with the Holy Spirit.

• He guaranteed our inheritance.

[Refrain]
Count your blessings, name them one by one:
Count your blessings, see what God hath done;
Count your blessings, name them one by one;
Count your many blessings, see what God hath done.

➤ 9. **Examine your life right now and see if any of the following difficult times are true of what you're experiencing. Check any or all that apply, or write your own.**

❑ a. I'm out on life's stormy sea, tempest-tossed.

❑ b. I'm discouraged, thinking all is lost.

❑ c. I'm burdened with a load of care.

❑ d. My cross is heavy to bear.

❑ e. I'm experiencing a time of conflict.

❑ f. Other: _____

❑ g. Now is not one of those difficult times. Thank the Lord!

➤ 10. **Suppose the members of your minichurch were to ask, "How can we pray for you?" What would you ask them to pray for you? Write a brief description of your prayer request.**

_____

_____

➤ 11. **Now, regardless of what difficulties you may be facing, take some time to count your blessings. Review and think about the spiritual blessings God has bestowed on you. Make some notes to yourself of other ways God has blessed your life. Consider the areas listed in the margin.**

**Other Areas of Blessing**

• your health and safety

• your family and relatives

• your job

• work associates

• food, shelter, clothes

• financial resources

• your church family

• the country or city in which you live

• ministry opportunities

• friends, neighbors

• others?

Other ways God has blessed me:

_____

_____

_____

_____

_____

Take some time to pray and thank God for the ways He has blessed your life. Be specific in naming the ways He has blessed you.

## Part 3: God the Father's Actions

**God the Father's Actions**

1. He chose you.
2. He adopted you.
3. He gave you grace.

In this letter, Paul stated three blessings of God the Father toward those who know Christ. If you have been born again by God's Spirit and by your faith in Christ, God has done the following things for you:

**God Chose You.** First, God the Father chose you in Christ before the creation of the world. Your salvation was not an afterthought with God. You were in His mind and heart before He created any part of this world or universe. He selected you to be His treasured possession. He chose you to be a special work of His creation that would bring Him glory and praise.

Have you ever stopped to think how wonderful it is to be chosen by the Creator and Ruler of the universe? Some people want to be chosen for a promotion at work. Others would like to be chosen to elected office. Some want a part in a blockbuster movie or to have their story told on national television. But no human position on earth is greater than the spiritual position for which you have been chosen. No human being or group on earth is greater than the heavenly Father, who knows you and has chosen you to be His. Glory! What a blessing to be chosen by God!

➤ 12. **What is one action of your heavenly Father? Fill in the blank.**

    1. He _____ me.

♦ **predestined:** marked out beforehand; determined in advance.

♦ **adopted:** placed in position as a son (child).

**God Adopted You.** Second, God the Father predestined us "to be adopted as his sons" (Eph. 1:5). As believers in Jesus Christ, we are God's children. He is our heavenly Father. Together, all believers are brothers and sisters in Christ—members of God's eternal family. With our adoption come the full rights, privileges, and inheritance of a child of God.

➤ 13. **What is a second action of your heavenly Father? Fill in the blank.**

    1. He chose me.

    2. He _____ me.

Some who read these words will feel warm and wonderful to know their heavenly Father desires to love them and spend time with them. Others may feel fear, uneasiness or even sickness at that thought. A common problem, even for Christians, is that a human father or father figure may have hurt them or failed to show love. This hurt may have come through a divorce, a death, a physical disability that resulted in neglect, abandonment, alcoholism, workaholism, rejection, verbal abuse, physical abuse, sexual abuse, or any number of other circumstances. Sometimes that hurt is an intentional act. Other times the hurt may have come just because of bad but unavoidable circumstances.

➤ 14. **Which of the following describes your feelings about your heavenly Father? Be honest. Check your response, or write your own.**
    ❑ I have warm and positive feelings about my relationship with Him.
    ❑ I have a slight uneasiness about it, but I don't know why.
    ❑ I have a slight uneasiness about it, and I do know why.
    ❑ I have a very negative feeling about it, and I don't know why.
    ❑ I have a very negative feeling about it, and I do know why.
    ❑ Other: _____

If you have a negative feeling about the idea of "father," don't let that keep you from experiencing the love of your heavenly Father. You don't necessarily need to know or understand why.

Your human father and other father figures are imperfect by the very nature of being human. Because of Christ, some have been able to love in a way that shows a godly love to their children. Because of sin, others may have damaged your idea of what a love relationship ought to be like.

God is the perfect example of unconditional love. His love is pure, trustworthy, and safe.

God, however, is the perfect example of unconditional love. His love is pure, trustworthy, and safe. You may know that in your mind but not feel it emotionally. If you've been hurt in the past, you need to experience the love of God in a way that touches your emotions. In just a moment, we'll give you an assignment that we pray will help you to do that. We pray you will not finish this course without being overwhelmed by the fact that your heavenly Father really loves YOU with a perfect love.

**God Gave You Grace.** Third, God's grace is unearned favor. He has freely bestowed on you His favor and acceptance. You didn't deserve it. You can't work to keep it. He gave you this gift through the One He loves—His one and only Son, Jesus Christ.

♦ **grace:** graciousness, the divine influence upon the heart and its reflection in the life, acceptable, benefit, favor, gift.

➤15. Read the definition of *grace* in the margin, and circle the word or phrase that best helps you understand what grace is.

➤16. What is a third action of your heavenly Father? Fill in the blank.

1. He chose me.

2. He adopted me.

3. He _____ me.

➤17. Though each of these blessings is precious—very special—which seems to be the greater to you or the most meaningful? Check one and briefly describe why.

❑ 1. Chosen      ❑ 2. Adopted      ❑ 3. Given Grace

Why?_____

_____

 18. **Special Assignment: A Walk/Talk with Your Heavenly Father.** Plan for time to take a walk or get out of your normal routine and spend some time with your heavenly Father. He has done so much for you. You are His child, and He wants to spend time with you. If you don't have time to get alone with your heavenly Father right now, plan to take some time later in the day or week. Plan for 30 minutes or more just to be with Him. Find a place where you can be alone—you might enjoy outside best, if that's possible. Spend the time in prayer. Talk to Him about anything that is on your heart and mind. Take time to listen to anything that He may want to reveal to you. You may even want to sing some songs of praise to Him as you spend time with Him. After your time alone with your heavenly Father, briefly describe your experience below.

_____

_____

_____

_____

## PART 4: RESPONDING TO GOD

**Debate It?** Some approach this message and suddenly get bogged down in a debate. Questions flood their minds—legitimate questions. For instance:

- If God chose us in Christ before the foundation of the world, how can I be free to choose?
- What good is it to tell others they can be saved if I don't know whom God has chosen?
- In other words, if God is sovereign, how can humanity have a free will?

Throughout church history, theologians have tried to explain in a logical way what Paul taught here. Unfortunately, they always end up, if they're honest, admitting there is no way to totally and logically explain all that Paul taught. We have what some call a biblical paradox, but the word *antinomy* might be better. Here Paul focused on two basic antinomies:

1. God is the sovereign and absolute ruler of the universe.

2. In His position as ruler, God has given humanity freedom to choose to follow Him or not.

The Bible teaches that all people are free to accept or reject the message of salvation. Jesus Christ died for the whole world (John 3:16). Whoever will may come! God chose us. He provided for our salvation. Then He offered it to us as a free gift. We, however, have the privilege and responsibility to receive this gift and surrender to His lordship or to reject it. We do have a choice, but we also must live with the consequences of our choice.

Many Christians miss the marvelous part of Paul's opening thoughts in Ephesians when they allow themselves to get bogged down trying to explain God and His sovereignty. His thoughts begin where ours end. But one thing we can believe and accept—even though we don't understand it all—and allow to transform our lives is this:

> "He chose us in him before the creation of the world to be holy and blameless in his sight. In love he predestined us to be adopted as his sons through Jesus Christ, in accordance with his pleasure and will—to the praise of his glorious grace, which he has freely given us in the One he loves" (Eph. 1:4-6).

🖑 **Pause to thank God that He chose you. Agree with Him that He is the Creator and has a right to rule His creation. If you have questions or concerns, tell Him about them. Ask Him to help you understand anything you need in order to have a right relationship with Him.**

How should a Christian respond to the truth Paul wrote about in this opening section of his letter? We don't need to spend all our time and energy debating it. Do you remember the refrain of the "hymn" we're studying? Our lives are to be "to the praise of his glory." Our best response should be twofold:

**1. Praise and Glorify God.** God has done wonderful things. He is worthy of our praise. We should praise and glorify Him. This is particularly true when we're facing difficult challenges and find ourselves in trying circumstances. While Paul was chained to a Roman guard, he wrote, "Praise be to the God and Father of our Lord Jesus Christ, who has blessed us in the heavenly realms with every spiritual blessing in Christ" (Eph. 1:3).

**2. Live a Worthy Life.** The greatest way for us to bring glory to God is through our lives. We should "live a life worthy" of this high and heavenly calling (Eph. 4:1). This

---

♦ **antinomy:** an apparent conflict between two equally valid ideas or principles.

**John 3:16**
"God so loved the world that he gave his one and only Son, that whoever believes in him shall not perish but have eternal life."

**Our Response to God**
1. Praise and glorify God.
2. Live a worthy life.

is where Paul was headed in his letter. But he stated it clearly right from the beginning when he wrote, "For he chose us in him before the creation of the world to be <u>holy</u> and <u>blameless</u> in his sight" (Eph. 1:4).

Some day we will be with God, and we will be conformed to the image of Jesus Christ completely. But it was never God's intention for us to wait until then to begin living a holy and righteous life. Paul made this point clear in his letter to Titus when he wrote, "For the grace of God that brings salvation has appeared to all men" and "it teaches us to say 'No' to ungodliness and worldly passions, and to live self-controlled, upright and godly lives in this present age" (Titus 2:11-12). This, of course, is what Paul was talking about in the opening part of this letter. He made it even clearer in chapter 2 when he wrote, "For it is by grace you have been saved, through faith—and this not from yourselves, it is the gift of God—not by works, so that no one can boast. For we are God's workmanship, created in Christ Jesus <u>to do good works</u>, which God prepared in advance for us to do" (Eph. 2:8-9).

➤ **19. If God were to give you a spiritual checkup, what do you think He would have to say about your life? Ask Him, and then check the response that seems to be closest to the way you believe God sees your life.**

❑ a. Your life is beginning to look like My Son. Continue to grow and live a worthy life. Your life reflects My glory. I'm pleased.

❑ b. You have a ways to go yet. Some areas of your life don't measure up to My standard of holiness. I want you to repent and allow Me to cleanse you. I have special purposes for you.

❑ c. Your life is far from what I desire you to be. I want you to be holy and blameless, but you must choose to die to sin. I can help you if you will turn to Me for help.

❑ d. You have not yet turned to My Son for forgiveness of sin. You still need to receive My gift of salvation. I've done all that's required, and the invitation to you is open. I look for the day when you will receive My gift of eternal life.

**Romans 12:1**

"I urge you, brothers, in view of God's mercy, to offer your bodies as living sacrifices, holy and pleasing to God—this is your spiritual act of worship.

_____

_____

_____

_____

_____

_____

A proper view of God's grace leads to righteousness—not unrighteousness. To be eternally secure in Christ should lead a Christian to present his body a living and holy sacrifice to God (Rom. 12:1). To do less is to spurn God's love, to reject the One who gave everything.

➤ **20. Take a moment to look back through this week's lesson. What have you learned or experienced this week about your relationship with God that has been most helpful or meaningful? Summarize it in the margin.**

Conclude your study in prayer:

• Praise and thank God the Father for all He has done for you.

• Ask the Father to help you better understand those things you may still have questions about.

• Pray for your minichurch members. Ask the Lord to prepare you for a special encounter with Him during your upcoming session together.

# MINICHURCH MEETING 2

## BEFORE THE MEETING

❑ 1. Turn to "Preparing for Your Minichurch Meeting" on page 143. Use it as a guide to get ready for this meeting. Check the box above after you have prepared.

❑ 2. Unless God should direct otherwise, your minichurch leader will be using the following outline to guide your meeting. You may want to look over the questions and activities so you will be better prepared to participate.

## DURING THE MEETING

❖ **Opening Prayer**

❖ **Singing Together**

Consider singing "Count Your Blessings" and "The Doxology" together with other choruses and hymns.

❖ **Building Relationships**

1. What things in God's creation cause you to praise Him most? Describe a time when something in creation caused you to praise God.

2. (p. 29, #11) What are some of the most meaningful ways God has blessed your life? Be specific as you discuss one or two with your group.

❖ **Praying for One Another** (in fours or sixes)

(p. 29) Discuss your responses to Activities 9 and 10. After one person speaks, one or more others should pray for him or her. Then let another speak, and pray for him. Continue until each has been prayed for.

❖ **Interacting with the Scriptures** (in fours or sixes)

1. What verse or passage of Scripture has been most meaningful or challenging to you this week? How has God used it to speak to you? What significant actions have you taken this week because of something God revealed through His Word?

2. (p. 26) Volunteers: Recite the memory verse you learned this week, and explain any special meaning you gained from it.

3. (p. 26, #5) What word or phrase from Ephesians 1:3-6 have you come to better understand or experience this week? Describe your understanding or experience.

❖ **Reviewing the Lesson**

1. (pp. 27-28) What are the ways God the Father has blessed you? God the Son? God the Spirit?

2. What does it mean to you to be chosen by God?

3. What does being adopted by God mean to you?

4. What is God's grace, and what difference does it make in your life?

❖ **Applying the Truths to Life**

1. What are some of the characteristics of a child of God that would show others our family resemblance?

2. (p. 30) Volunteers, give your response to #14. How has your family experience influenced your relationship with your heavenly Father?

3. Volunteers: How has your experience with your heavenly Father revealed characteristics of His love: unconditional, pure, trustworthy, safe, and so forth?

4. (p. 31, #17) Which of the blessings of your heavenly Father seems to be most meaningful to you, and why?

5. (p. 31, #18) Volunteers: What did you experience during your walk and talk with your heavenly Father? How could future times like this make a difference in your experience of a love relationship with Him?

6. Has this lesson caused you to want to praise and glorify God more than normal? Why?

7. In what ways has God given you a greater desire to live "holy and blameless in his sight"?

8. (p. 33) Volunteers: Based on the way you responded to #19, how can we pray for you now and in the days to come? (Group: Pause to pray for each person who has a prayer request.)

❖ **Responding to God in Prayer**

Pray short or sentence prayers thanking God for His blessings. Be specific in naming the spiritual blessings as Paul did. Name other ways God has blessed you in your thanksgiving to Him. Pray as many times each as time allows.

❖ **Ministering to One Another**

What needs (if any) of members have you become aware of during this meeting that the Body needs to care for? What can we do to meet the needs or to help connect the person with those who can help? Are there things we need to do this week to help?

❖ **Reaching Out to Others**

Are there people in your circles of influence who need a saving relationship with Jesus Christ and for whom God seems to be giving you a special burden? What can we pray or do to help you carry that burden?

❖ **Closing Prayer**

❖ **Optional: "Breaking Bread" Together**

# LOOKING UP TO GOD THE SON

**Saved by the Blood**

On the day Max Walsh left the warmth of a mountain lodge in the Austrian Alps, the weather was "friendly." But the weather changed suddenly. Max found himself in a blinding snowstorm. Losing all sense of direction, he finally was overcome by the cold and collapsed.

The owner of the lodge sent his best dog to look for Max. Following his God-created instincts, the well-trained dog soon discovered him. The dog grabbed the sleeve of Max's frozen jacket and began to jerk and pull. Max started to regain his senses and mistook the dog for a wolf. Fear gripped him! Pulling his hunting knife from his sheath, he reached out and stabbed his would-be savior.

Badly wounded, the dog let go and limped back to the lodge, where he fell dead at his master's feet. Sensing what had happened, the owner of the lodge made his way through the blizzard, carefully following the trail of blood. He found Max, once again in a semiconscious state, and was able to carry him back to the safety of the lodge, where he survived. Max's life was saved because a faithful dog carried out his master's command, literally shedding his blood in the process.

Many of us listen to a story like this and are moved to tears. Do you ever wonder why we're so emotionally moved by dog stories and yet we're so unmoved at times by the story of the One who shed His blood that we might live? Jesus Christ, the Son of God, went to the cross and shed His blood for us, for you.

➤1. **On the cross to the left, draw a simple picture of Jesus on the cross. If you have a red pen or marker, use it (otherwise use your pencil or pen) to draw blood on Jesus:**
   - **on His head, where the crown of thorns pierced His brow**
   - **on His hands and feet, where the nails were driven**
   - **on His shoulders and sides, where the whips drew blood**
   - **on His side, where the soldier's spear drew the final blood**

 **After you read Luke 22:20 below the cross, pause to pray. Express your love to Jesus for the blood He shed for you. Ask Him to help you during this lesson to better understand all He has done to provide for your salvation.**

"This cup is the new testament in my blood, which is shed for you" (Luke 22:20, KJV).

As we saw in last week's lesson, God the Father planned our salvation (Eph. 1:3-6). In this lesson, we see that Jesus Christ, God's Son, was the One who carried out God's plan. We want to help you look up to the cross to behold the Savior of the world. But more important, we trust you'll look beyond the cross to the resurrected Christ, who is seated in the heavenlies at the right hand of God the Father.

## PART 1: INTERACTING WITH THE SCRIPTURE

### Reading / Hearing God's Word

**Read or Listen to:**
- ❏ Ephesians 1–6
- ❏ Ephesians 1–3
- ❏ Ephesians 1:1-23

➤2. Select one of the reading (or listening) options in the margin. Using your Bible, read or listen to the passage of Scripture. As you begin, ask God to speak to you through His Word. Watch for one verse or idea that is especially meaningful to you today. Once you finish reading, check the box indicating the passage you read.

### Meditating on God's Word

➤3. In the margin, write a brief summary of the meaningful verse or idea you just identified.

**Meaningful Verse or Idea**

_____

_____

_____

### Memorizing God's Word

➤4. Select and tear out a new Scripture memory card from the back of your book, or continue reviewing one you started learning earlier. For a new verse, use the tips for memorizing Scripture on your bookmark.

### Understanding God's Word

➤5. Read again the focal passage for this week's lesson (Eph. 1:7-12) in the margin. Underline any key phrases or ideas that seem especially meaningful. Then read the brief definitions of key words below. This will prepare you for the remainder of this week's study.

**Ephesians 1:7-12**

"In him we have redemption through his blood, the forgiveness of sins, in accordance with the riches of God's grace that he lavished on us with all wisdom and understanding. And he made known to us the mystery of his will according to his good pleasure, which he purposed in Christ, to be put into effect when the times will have reached their fulfillment—to bring all things in heaven and on earth together under one head, even Christ.

"In him we were also chosen, having been predestined according to the plan of him who works out everything in conformity with the purpose of his will, in order that we, who were the first to hope in Christ, might be for the praise of his glory."

- ♦ **redemption:** ransom in full from bondage, bought at a price and released.
- ♦ **forgiveness:** to carry or send away, to be gracious toward, to let loose.
- ♦ **sin:** a side-slip, deviation, error, offense, fault, missing the mark.
- ♦ **wisdom:** understanding the true nature of things.
- ♦ **understanding:** intellectual or moral insight, prudence.
- ♦ **mystery:** a divine secret that has been or is being revealed.
- ♦ **chosen:** selected as a kindness or favor.
- ♦ **predestined:** to limit or set out in advance, determine before.
- ♦ **hope:** confident expectation, assurance of what is to come.
- ♦ **glory:** evidence of God's wonderful work or character, honor.

➤6. Look back through this list of words. Circle one that you would like to understand or experience more fully.

### Looking through the Scripture to God

 Now pause to pray.
- Thank God for what He has done for you through His Son, Jesus Christ. Thank Him for your redemption and forgiveness.
- Thank Him for the grace He has lavished on you.
- Ask Him to continue to increase your wisdom and understanding.
- Ask the Father to bring everything—including your life—under the lordship of Christ. Agree with Jesus that He is your "Head."
- Thank God that He has a plan for your life. Ask Him to help you understand what that plan is and how you can cooperate with Him to see it come to pass.
- Ask the Lord to help you bring Him praise and glory through your life.
- Close by praying Ephesians 1:17-19 and 3:16-19 (on your bookmark) for yourself and your minichurch.

## PART 2: GOD THE SON'S ACTION

**Ephesians 1:3-6**

"Praise be to the God and Father of our Lord Jesus Christ, who has blessed us in the heavenly realms with every spiritual blessing in Christ. For he chose us in him before the creation of the world to be holy and blameless in his sight. In love he predestined us to be adopted as his sons through Jesus Christ, in accordance with his pleasure and will—to the praise of his glorious grace, which he has freely given us in the One he loves."

Although verses 7–10 bring the work of Christ into sharp focus, the Son of God's part in our salvation appears throughout this introductory section.

- Jesus Christ is the means whereby we receive God's spiritual blessings (Eph. 1:3).
- God chose us in Christ before He actually created the world (Eph. 1:4).
- We were adopted as God's children through Jesus Christ (Eph. 1:5).
- His glorious grace was freely given us "in the One He loves"—none other than Jesus Christ (Eph. 1:6).

Paul next spoke of the specific action taken by Christ to make our salvation possible. He shed His blood on Calvary's cross. Thus Paul wrote, "In him we have redemption through his blood, the forgiveness of sins, in accordance with the riches of God's grace that he lavished on us with all wisdom and understanding" (Eph. 1:7-8).

➤ **7. Fill in the blank to state the primary work of Christ on your behalf.**

Jesus Christ shed His _____ for me.

Some people hear the message of the cross and respond with antagonism. In fact, some have referred to the message of the Bible as a "slaughterhouse religion" because of the role of blood. In their pride and arrogance, they believe they have progressed beyond what they identify as a primitive approach to spiritual truth. The fact remains that the sovereign Creator of the universe chose to forgive your sins through the shedding of His own Son's blood.

"Without the shedding of blood there is no forgiveness."

Why did God choose to save us through the shedding of blood? The Bible says that "the wages of sin is death" (Rom. 6:23). God considers sin so serious that a life must be given because of it. Scripture also tells us that "the life of the flesh is in the blood" (Lev. 17:11, KJV). In the Old Testament, when the blood of a lamb was shed, it symbolized that a life had been given for sin. In the New Testament, the blood of God's Lamb, Jesus Christ, was shed for the same reason. In Hebrews 9:22 we read, "Without the shedding of blood there is no forgiveness." Not only has God provided forgiveness through the shedding of blood, but He also has done many other things through the blood of Christ.

➤ **8. Match what God did through the blood of Christ in the left margin with the scripture below. Write the number beside the letter.**

1. He bought the church.

2. He justified us.

3. He freed us from our sins.

4. He cleanses our consciences from acts that lead to death.

5. He made peace.

6. He brought us near.

7. He purifies us from all sin.

___ a. "Since we have now been justified by his <u>blood</u>, how much more shall we be saved from God's wrath through him!" (Rom. 5:9).

___ b. "But now in Christ Jesus you who once were far away have been brought near through the <u>blood</u> of Christ" (Eph. 2:13).

___ c. "Be shepherds of the church of God, which he bought with his own <u>blood</u>" (Acts 20:28).

___ d. "If we walk in the light, as he is in the light, we have fellowship with one another, and the <u>blood</u> of Jesus, his Son, purifies us from every sin" (1 John 1:7).

___ e. "To him who loves us and has freed us from our sins by his <u>blood</u>" (Rev. 1:5).

___ f. "For God was pleased to have all his fullness dwell in him, and through him to reconcile to himself all things . . . by making peace through his <u>blood</u>, shed on the cross" (Col. 1:19-20).

___ g. "How much more, then, will the <u>blood</u> of Christ . . . cleanse our consciences from acts that lead to death, so that we may serve the living God!" (Heb. 9:14).

(Check your answers: a-2; b-6; c-1; d-7; e-3; f-5; g-4.)

**Some of God's Work
Through Christ's Blood**

- He brings you near.
- He cleanses your conscience.
- He forgives your sin.
- He frees you from sin.
- He justifies you.
- He makes peace with you.
- He makes you holy.
- He purifies you.

We also read that God makes you holy through Christ's blood: "Jesus also suffered outside the city gate to make the people holy through his own blood" (Heb. 13:12).

 **Pause and thank God that He loved you enough to pay such a high price for your forgiveness. Thank Him for the things He did through the blood of Christ—we've listed some in the margin.**

Ever since Christ's death on the cross, the blood has been precious to believers. This is reflected in many of our favorite hymns.

 **Read (or sing if you know the tune) the verses of the following hymns, and spend time worshiping the Lord for all He has done for you.**

Alas, and did my Saviour bleed
And did my Sovereign die?
Would He devote that sacred head
For sinners such as I?

**At the Cross**
by Isaac Watts
(refrain by Ralph E. Hudson)

[Refrain]
At the cross, at the cross where I first saw the light,
And the burden of my heart rolled away,
It was there by faith I received my sight,
And now I am happy all the day!

**There Is a Fountain**
by William Cowper

There is a fountain filled with blood
Drawn from Emmanuel's veins;
And sinners plunged beneath that flood,
Lose all their guilty stains.

The dying thief rejoiced to see
That fountain in his day;
And there may I, though vile as he,
Wash all my sins away.

Dear dying Lamb, Thy precious blood
Shall never lose its power
Till all the ransomed Church of God
Be saved, to sin no more.

**There Is Power in the Blood**
by Lewis E. Jones

Would you be free from the burden of sin?
There's power in the blood, power in the blood;
Would you o'er evil a victory win?
There's wonderful power in the blood.

Would you be whiter, much whiter than snow?
There's power in the blood, power in the blood;
Sin-stains are lost in its life-giving flow;
There's wonderful power in the blood.

Would you do service for Jesus, your King?
There's power in the blood, power in the blood;
Would you live daily His praises to sing?
There's wonderful power in the blood.

## PART 3: A BELIEVER'S BENEFITS

OUR SPIRITUAL BLESSINGS

• He redeemed us.

• He provided forgiveness for our sins.

• He lavished grace on us with all wisdom and understanding.

• He made known to us the mystery of His will.

◆ redemption: ransom in full from bondage, bought at a price and released.

In Lesson 2 you identified the spiritual benefits described in Ephesians 1:7-12. They are listed again in the margin for you. We want to focus attention on two of these blessings. Christ has redeemed you and He has provided for forgiveness of your sins. Paul said we "have <u>redemption</u> through his blood, the <u>forgiveness</u> of sins" (Eph. 1:7).

**Redemption.** This term may seem strange, but we use the word *redeem* in our day as well. We redeem coupons, savings bonds, and even soda cans for their deposit. If you were to take an item to a pawn shop, the owner would give you an amount of money for the item and a claim ticket. If you wanted to get the item back, you would take your ticket back to the shop and pay the "redemption" price.

▶9. **Read the definition of *redemption* in the margin. Then write a brief definition of your own below.**

_____

_____

The religious concept of being "redeemed" has its roots in the Old Testament. Its basic meaning has to do with being released from the state of servitude or bondage. The release came when someone paid the price for the slave's freedom. The greatest Old Testament picture of redemption is seen in what God did to set His people free from Egypt, where they were slaves. This bondage continued approximately 400 years. God brought plagues on Egypt in order to set His people free. The final plague was that "every firstborn son in Egypt" had to die—including the "firstborn of the cattle as well" (Ex. 11:5).

For God's people to be delivered from the plague, God gave them special instructions. All families were to select a lamb, free from any defect, slaughter this animal, and have a special meal called "the LORD's Passover" (Ex. 12:11). However, they were "to take some of the blood and put it on the sides and tops of the door frames of the houses" where they had eaten the lambs (Ex. 12:7). The Lord said,

> "I will pass through Egypt and strike down every firstborn—both men and animals—and I will bring judgment on all the gods of Egypt; I am the LORD. The blood will be a sign for you on the houses where you are; and when I see the blood, I will pass over you. No destructive plague will touch you when I strike Egypt" (Ex. 12:12-13).

▶10. **What price did Israelite families have to pay to be protected from the death angel? Check one.**
   ❑ a. Thirty shekels per person.
   ❑ b. The death of their firstborn son so others would not die.
   ❑ c. The death of a sacrificial lamb.

**Hebrews 9:12**

"He did not enter by means of the blood of goats and calves; but he entered the Most Holy Place once for all by his own blood, having obtained eternal redemption."

A sacrificial lamb had to die so its blood could be placed over the door. This Old Testament event is a graphic picture of Christ's redemptive work on your behalf. This event (and later the whole sacrificial system set up for Israel) pointed to the shed blood of Jesus Christ. John the Baptist recognized this truth: "John saw Jesus coming toward him and said, 'Look, the Lamb of God, who takes away the sin of the world!'" (John 1:29). The New Testament letter to the Hebrews made this point crystal clear: "Without the shedding of blood there is no forgiveness" (Heb. 9:22). But Jesus obtained redemption through His blood (Heb. 9:12).

➤11. **What is one benefit Christ provided for believers? Fill in the blank.**

Christ provided for my _____ by His blood.

**Forgiveness.** Christ paid the price that could set mankind free from sin's bondage. By doing so, He can now offer forgiveness. Divine "forgiveness" and "redemption" are hand-in-glove concepts; they go together.

To be forgiven by God means that He no longer holds our sins against us. God said, "I will forgive their wickedness and will remember their sins no more" (Heb. 8:12). The blood of Christ has paid the price for all sin—past, present, and future. When we become believers, the blood of Christ keeps on cleansing us from sin (1 John 1:9). If it didn't, we would not have eternal salvation. If it weren't for Christ's finished work on the cross, the smallest sin would result in eternal separation from God.

What happens, then, when a believer sins? Here's a quick lesson:
- The Bible teaches that we will be disciplined by the Lord but never condemned with the world (1 Cor. 11:31-32).
- God deals seriously with sin. We should never use our freedom as a permission to sin (Rom. 6:1-2, 15, 18; Gal. 5:13).
- A Christian is to be dead to sin and set free from it (Rom. 6:2, 1 Pet. 2:24). We don't have to sin—we have a choice.
- If we do sin, however, we need to confess (agree with God about) our sins. God then forgives and restores us to fellowship with Him (1 John 1:9).

➤12. **If you haven't already done so, read the scriptures in the margin that were referred to above. Mark the following statements "T" for true and "F" for false.**

_____ 1. Once a person becomes a Christian, he will never again commit an act of sin.

_____ 2. If a Christian does sin, God will discipline him if he doesn't confess his sin and return to God and His ways.

_____ 3. A Christian can live in righteousness and does not have to sin.

_____ 4. Since God forgives us, we can go ahead and enjoy sin all we want.

_____ 5. Sin is serious with God because it cost Him the blood of His Son to forgive it.

(Answers: 1-F; 2-T; 3-T; 4-F; 5-T)

➤13. **How have you responded to Christ's forgiveness in the past? Check your response.**

❏ a. I've taken His forgiveness too lightly and been too casual about sin in my life. "Lord, I'm sorry."

❏ b. I've tried to take His forgiveness seriously. I seek to live free from sin. "Lord, thank You for helping me."

*Conclude this part of your lesson thanking the Lord for your redemption and forgiveness. Thank Him for what He has done for you.*

## Sidebar

### Sin and Forgiveness

**1 Corinthians 11:31-32**

"If we judged ourselves, we would not come under judgment. When we are judged by the Lord, we are being disciplined so that we will not be condemned with the world."

**Romans 6:1-2, 15, 18**

"Shall we go on sinning so that grace may increase? By no means! We died to sin; how can we live in it any longer? . . .

"Shall we sin because we are not under law but under grace? By no means! . . . You have been set free from sin and have become slaves to righteousness."

**Galatians 5:13**

"You, my brothers, were called to be free. But do not use your freedom to indulge the sinful nature."

**1 Peter 2:24**

"He himself bore our sins in his body on the tree, so that we might die to sins and live for righteousness; by his wounds you have been healed."

**1 John 1:9**

"If we confess our sins, he is faithful and just and will forgive us our sins and purify us from all unrighteousness."

## Part 4: Responding to God

God has richly blessed us with spiritual blessings. We need to ask ourselves the following questions:

- How should a Christian respond to such love—to "the riches of God's grace that he lavished on us with all wisdom and understanding" (Eph. 1:7-8)?
- How should God's children respond to the fact that God has "made known to us the mystery of his will according to his good pleasure, which he purposed in Christ" (Eph. 1:9)?
- How should we respond as those who have been a part of God's great plan that He has "put into effect" (Eph. 1:10)?
- How should we respond to the fact that "we are also chosen, having been predestined according to the plan of him who works out everything in conformity with the purpose of his will" (Eph. 1:11)?

Paul answered these questions in the hymn refrain we studied last week. Our lives are to be lived in such a way that we "might be for the praise of his glory" (Eph. 1:12). Not only should we lift our hearts and voices in praise to God, but our very lives should show God's glory. Your life should reflect the quality of God's mighty work and character.

➤ 14. **When people observe your life, what do you think they see of God's glory? Check your response or write your own.**
- ❑ a. They realize God is a wonderful and powerful God.
- ❑ b. They see some of God's glory, but it's tarnished and somewhat hidden by the dirt and grime in my life.
- ❑ c. They wonder if God has anything at all to do with my life.
- ❑ d. They get a distorted view of what God is like.
- ❑ e. Other:_____

When we truly understand the love of Christ in providing redemption and forgiveness, it can't help but affect our relationship to God and others.

**Your Relationship to God.** Some who are studying this course will get to this point and realize they have never understood or accepted God's gift of eternal life. Perhaps as we've looked at the spiritual blessings God gives, you realize you have not received those blessings.

➤ 15. **Have you come to the place in your spiritual life where you know for sure that you have received God's gift of eternal life?**
- ❑ Yes, I have received God's gift, and the Spirit of His Son lives in me.
- ❑ No, I have not received God's free gift.
- ❑ I'm not sure where I stand with God.

➤ 16. **If you're not sure or if you realize you have not accepted God's offer of redemption and salvation, turn to page 8. Read Parts 2 and 3. We pray this might be the time you would be ready to accept God's free gift.**

**Your Relationship with Others.** Christ is not only our Savior from sin, but He's also our example in the area of human forgiveness. Have you forgiven others who have sinned against you? This is a very practical application for every Christian. Listen to the words of Paul: "Bear with each other and forgive whatever grievances you may have against one another. Forgive as the Lord forgave you" (Col. 3:13).

In the Sermon on the Mount, Jesus explained the importance of forgiving others: "If you forgive men when they sin against you, your heavenly Father will also forgive you. But if you do not forgive men their sins, your Father will not forgive your sins" (Matt. 6:14-15).

➤ 17. **Based on these statements from Paul and Jesus, what do you need to do in your relationships with others? Fill in the blank.**

I need to _____ others when they sin against me.

➤ 18. **If God were to evaluate your life right now based on how you forgive others, how would He forgive you? Check your response.**
   ❑ a. As best I know, I have forgiven all who have sinned against me. God promises He will forgive me in the same way.
   ❑ b. I've got one or more people who really hurt me, and I haven't forgiven them. God says He is waiting to forgive me until I forgive.

When you become a child of God, He places the Spirit of His Son in you. We will study more about the Holy Spirit next week. He can enable you to forgive even when your human nature would tell you not to do it.

➤ 19. **If you realize you need to forgive some people, ask the Lord to help you. Express your forgiveness of them to Him. If you need to call or visit someone to express your forgiveness, do that as soon as you get a chance. Though this is hard, think about the way God has forgiven you. Jesus had to shed His blood for you. Remember that your forgiveness by God is waiting on your forgiveness of others.**

**Your Service for God.** Because of what God has done for you, your natural response should include a life of service to Him. In Romans 12:1, Paul said, "I urge you, brothers, in view of God's mercy, to offer your bodies as living sacrifices, holy and pleasing to God—this is your spiritual act of worship." God wants your life to be lived as an offering to Him.

➤ 20. **Read the story of "Stenberg's Painting of Christ" on the next page. As you do, look for the words he placed below his painting of Christ in the art gallery of Dusseldorf. Underline them. Read the story before continuing.**

❦

Stenburg's painting no longer exists. It was burned when the Dusseldorf art gallery was destroyed by fire. But the story even to this day is not ended. The painting's influence will live on and on through the lives of those who were touched and through the story as it's retold. And the question placed below his painting of Christ still calls for our response today.

"All this I did for thee; what hast thou done for me?"

➤ 21. **How would you respond to this question? Begin recording below or in the margin some of the ways you have expressed love for the Lord through your life.**

_____

_____

_____

_____

_____

_____

## STENBURG'S PAINTING OF CHRIST

One day a priest climbed the stairs in an old building in Dusseldorf, Germany, and knocked on the door. He had come to ask the artist Stenburg if he would paint an altarpiece for the Church of Saint Jerome. The artist thought the matter over carefully and decided to do it. Little by little, a picture of Christ dying for the sins of the world emerged on his canvas.

As the months rolled by, Stenburg started to experience a spirit of unrest. Spring had come, and the artist decided to lay his brushes aside for a while. He took his sketchbook in hand and began roaming through the hills and valleys.

One day on the edge of the forest, he came upon a young gypsy girl. She was sitting in the grass weaving daisy chains. Her beauty immediately captured his heart. He saw in her great potential. In a matter of minutes, he convinced her that she should come to his studio, where he could paint her as a little Spanish dancing girl.

The first day she arrived in the studio, she noticed the emerging altarpiece. Her mind immediately was flooded with questions.

"Who is that?" she asked.

"The Christ," Stenburg responded nonchalantly.

"What are they doing to Him?" she continued.

"Crucifying Him," Stenburg replied with disinterest.

"But who are those people? Those people with all the ugly faces?" Her interest was growing, and Stenburg was irritated. He told her to stop asking questions and pose for him. And so she did.

However, the little girl's interest could not be stifled. So one day when Stenburg seemed to be in a positive mood, she ventured another question.

"Why did they do that to Him? Was He very bad?"

"No!" the old artist responded sharply. "He was actually very good!"

Stenburg realized he had to answer the little girl's questions once and for all. He laid down his brushes and told the story of Christ's crucifixion, warning her at the end of the story not to ask any more questions.

Finally the day arrived when Stenburg had completed his painting of the little gypsy girl. In that final moment before leaving, she took one long, hard look at the picture of Christ. As she turned to leave, she looked up into the artist's eyes and said, "You must love Him more than anything else in this world since He has done all that for you." And then she disappeared out the door and down the stairs.

Stenburg was startled! *Love Him?* he asked himself. *I don't love Him!*

The gypsy girl's final words became an obsession in Stenburg's mind, however. He couldn't forget them. Every morning when he walked into his studio and saw the picture of Christ, the words surfaced in his mind: *You must love Him more than anything else in this world since He has done all that for you.*

Stenburg was relieved when he finally completed the altarpiece and it was placed in the Church of Saint Jerome. He thought its absence would solve his problem. But it didn't! He found no rest in heart and soul.

Finally, after days of unrest, he discovered some special religious meetings were being held in a home on the outskirts of Dusseldorf. *Perhaps I can find my answers there*, he thought.

Stenburg made his way to a home where once again he heard the story of the death of Christ. This time, however, it took on new meaning. He saw that Christ had died for him. He put his faith in Christ for salvation and became a Christian. It was then he was captured with a new desire. He wanted to do something for his Lord. He now truly loved Jesus Christ!

Stenburg thought long and hard about what he might do to express his love for His Savior. After asking God for direction, the thought flashed through his mind: *I cannot express the love of God by the use of words, but with His help I can paint it.*

The face of Christ on the cross he had painted for the Church of Saint Jerome was full of agony and pain. But the picture of Christ he would now paint would be full of love.

Love burned in his own soul as he worked. The picture slowly emerged, showing the head and shoulders of Christ with a crown of thorns on His brow. It was a beautiful and inspiring picture. The eyes of Christ held the beholder spellbound. They were full of tender, eternal love.

When the picture was completed, Stenburg would not sell it. He gave it to the city of Dusseldorf, and it was hung in the art gallery. Under the painting he placed these words: "All this I did for thee; what hast thou done for me?"

Thousands came and stood in front of the picture. As they looked, tears filled their eyes. Often Stenburg would go to the gallery and watch the people who stood before it. As he watched, he prayed that God would speak to them through the picture.

One day as he was watching, a young woman came into the gallery. She stationed herself before the picture, and the artist could see that she was crying. She remained so long that at last he went to speak to her. As she turned and faced him, Stenburg recognized the little gypsy girl—now a young woman—who had posed for him several years before. "I often come to look at Him," she said. With quivering lips she added, "I wish He had loved me like that, but I'm only a gypsy."

Immediately Stenburg asked her forgiveness. He apologized for not having told the story accurately when she first asked her questions in his studio. With the girl's astonished eyes upon him, he told the story once again. But this time he explained the true meaning of the cross. And there in the art gallery, the gypsy girl gave her heart to the Savior.

One day a young nobleman entered the gallery and stood weeping before the picture. He was a Christian man, yet up to this time his life had not counted much for God. The painting with the words beneath sank into his heart: "All this I did for thee; what hast thou done for me?"

That day that young nobleman laid his life and fortune at the feet of the Son of God. His name was Count Nikolaus von Zinzendorf. Later he became the founder of the Moravian mission, which touched the world with the gospel. These Moravian missionaries soon touched another young man named John Wesley, who went on to lead in the First Great Awakening, where many people came to know the saving love of the Savior.

43

# MINICHURCH MEETING 3

## BEFORE THE MEETING

❑ 1. Turn to "Preparing for Your Minichurch Meeting" on page 143. Use it as a guide to get ready for this meeting. Check the box above after you have prepared.

❑ 2. Unless God should direct otherwise, your minichurch leader will be using the following outline to guide your meeting. You may want to look over the questions and activities so you will be better prepared to participate.

## DURING THE MEETING

❖ **Opening Prayer**

❖ **Singing Together**

1. Volunteer: Give a brief testimony about what the blood of Jesus means to you.
2. Consider singing "At the Cross," "There Is a Fountain," and "There Is Power in the Blood" together with other choruses and hymns.

❖ **Building Relationships**

1. Volunteers: When and how did you come to recognize your need for Jesus and place your faith and trust in Him? What person most influenced your decision to follow Jesus?
2. Other Volunteers: When and how did you come to sense God wanted you to join (or have a relationship with) our church (or minichurch)?

❖ **Responding to God in Prayer** (in fours or sixes)

Take turns praying brief but specific prayers thanking God for His saving grace. Thank Him for what He has done through Jesus to provide for your redemption and forgiveness. Thank Him for particular people and experiences He used to bring you to Himself.

❖ **Interacting with the Scriptures** (in fours or sixes)

1. What verse or passage of Scripture has been most meaningful or challenging to you this week? How has God used it to speak to you? What significant actions have you taken this week because of something God revealed through His Word? Were there people you had to forgive (p. 42)?
2. (p. 36) Volunteers: Recite the memory verse you learned this week, and explain any special meaning you gained from it.
3. (p. 36, #6) What word or phrase from Ephesians 1:7-12 have you come to better understand or experience this week? Describe your understanding or experience.

❖ **Reviewing the Lesson**

1. (p. 37, #8) What are some things God accomplished

through the blood of Christ? What difference do these actions make in the life of a believer or a church?

2. (p. 39) What does *redemption* mean, and how did God accomplish our redemption through Jesus?
3. (p. 40) Once a Christian is saved and forgiven, what relationship does he or she have to sin? Review and discuss the answers to #12. Consider reading Romans 6 aloud to understand this relationship more clearly.
4. (pp. 41-42) What kind of forgiveness of others does God expect of us?

❖ **Applying the Truths to Life**

1. How can a person's life bring praise and glory to God? How can a church bring God praise and glory?
2. (p. 41) Volunteers: How did you respond to #14? What's the greatest evidence in your life that God has been at work?
3. (p. 42) Why is forgiveness of others so difficult for us? How does the Spirit of Christ in us help us to forgive?
4. Volunteers: What individuals or groups do you have a hard time forgiving? Have you become bitter and unforgiving? How can we pray with you and for you?
5. (p. 42, #20) How have you expressed your love for Jesus through your actions? How can a person "love" Jesus when He's in heaven? (See Matt. 25:34-45 and John 14:15-24.)
6. In what ways can a Christian offer his or her life as a "living sacrifice" (Rom. 12:1) to God?

❖ **Praying for One Another** (in fours or sixes)

1. Take some time to offer glory and praise to God for what you see of His handiwork in the lives of those in your group.
2. Invite individuals to say how your group can pray for their spiritual concerns. After one states a request, two or more should pray for this person and his request.

❖ **Ministering to One Another**

What needs (if any) of members have you become aware of during this meeting that the Body needs to care for? What can we do to meet the needs or to help connect the person with those who can help? Are there things we need to do this week to help?

❖ **Reaching Out to Others**

Are there people in your circles of influence who need a saving relationship with Jesus Christ and for whom God seems to be giving you a special burden? What can we pray or do to help you carry that burden?

❖ **Closing Prayer**

❖ **Optional: "Breaking Bread" Together**

# LOOKING UP TO GOD THE SPIRIT

### The Engagement Ring

### Revelation 19:6-9

"Then I heard what sounded like a great multitude, like the roar of rushing waters and like loud peals of thunder, shouting: 'Hallelujah! For our Lord God Almighty reigns. Let us rejoice and be glad and give him glory! For the wedding of the Lamb has come, and his bride has made herself ready. Fine linen, bright and clean, was given her to wear.' (Fine linen stands for the righteous acts of the saints.)

"Then the angel said to me, 'Write: "Blessed are those who are invited to the wedding supper of the Lamb!"'"

(Gene's story) More than a quarter of a century ago, I picked up a lovely young lady in my freshly washed 1941 Chevrolet coupe. Elaine and I were spending the day together, heading for a recreational area in central Illinois. A couple of months before, I had asked her to be my wife. She had accepted.

As we headed south that day, she had no idea that a special gift was hidden away in a box of candy. I had carefully taken the cellophane from the box, removed a few chocolates from the center, and replaced them with a ring box wrapped in foil. Inside the box was an engagement ring. When it was safely tucked away with the other "goodies," it looked like a huge chocolate mint. I then replaced the cellophane, sealed the edges with a hot iron, and placed the box in the glove compartment. It looked as though it had just come off the drugstore shelf.

While we were driving along, I casually—but with my heart pounding—told Elaine I had bought some candy to munch on as we traveled. Totally unaware of what was about to happen, she finally got the wrapper off the box and opened it. I glanced at the open box, nearly dying inside, and said, "That one in the center looks large enough for both of us to eat. Why don't we share it first?" Unsuspectingly, Elaine took out what she thought was a gigantic piece of chocolate, removed the wrapping, and . . . you can imagine the look on her face. The ring was totally unexpected, since I had told her I was working toward getting it as a Christmas gift. But here it was a month early—on her birthday.

Neither of us will forget that moment together. When she placed the ring on her finger, our engagement was official! The ring was, in a sense, a "down payment" or "deposit" guaranteeing that Elaine was to become my wife and I her husband. It was no longer just a verbal agreement between us. Furthermore, it became a public fact. Everywhere we went, people would see we were engaged.

Paul told us, in Ephesians 1:13-14, that when God sent His Spirit to indwell His people, the Spirit was a "deposit"—a down payment—guaranteeing our inheritance until the redemption of those who are God's possession. In fact, the Greek word translated "deposit" was actually used, on occasion, to refer to a wedding ring.

In Revelation 19:6-9, we're told that the Bride of Christ (the Church) will participate in the Marriage Supper of the Lamb (Christ). Believers, we'll be there for the wedding feast. We weren't given an engagement ring, but we have been given the Holy Spirit to guarantee that our eternal future with God is going to take place.

 **As you begin this lesson, read Revelation 19:6-9 in the margin. Reflect on what that wedding day will be like. Think about the joy of the bride. Ask the Lord to help you this week to come to a clear understanding of what He has done through the Holy Spirit to seal the promise He made to those He chose as His people. Express to the Lord Jesus your love for Him and your anticipation of the wedding.**

## PART 1: INTERACTING WITH THE SCRIPTURE

### Reading / Hearing God's Word

**Read or Listen to:**
- ❑ Ephesians 1–6
- ❑ Ephesians 1–3
- ❑ Ephesians 1:1-23

➤1. Select one of the reading (or listening) options in the margin. Using your Bible, read or listen to the passage of Scripture. As you begin, ask God to speak to you through His Word. Watch for one verse or idea that's especially meaningful to you today. Once you finish reading, check the box indicating the passage you read.

### Meditating on God's Word

**Meaningful Verse or Idea**

_____

_____

_____

➤2. In the margin, write a brief summary of the meaningful verse or idea you just identified.

### Memorizing God's Word

➤3. Select and tear out a new Scripture memory card from the back of your book, or continue reviewing the one you started learning earlier. For a new verse, use the tips for memorizing Scripture on your bookmark.

### Understanding God's Word

➤4. Read again the focal passage for this week's lesson (Eph. 1:13-14) in the margin. Underline any key phrases or ideas that seem especially meaningful to you. Then read the brief definitions of key words below. This will prepare you for the remainder of this week's study.

**Ephesians 1:13-14**
"You also were included in Christ when you heard the word of truth, the gospel of your salvation. Having believed, you were marked in him with a seal, the promised Holy Spirit, who is a deposit guaranteeing our inheritance until the redemption of those who are God's possession—to the praise of his glory."

- ♦ **truth:** that which is true, ultimate reality.
- ♦ **gospel:** a good message, good news.
- ♦ **salvation:** rescue, safety, deliverance from the eternal penalty of death for sin.
- ♦ **believe:** to have faith in, upon, or with respect to; to entrust one's spiritual well-being to Christ, commit, trust.
- ♦ **seal:** stamp with a signet or private mark for security or showing ownership.
- ♦ **deposit:** earnest, a pledge given in advance as security for the rest.
- ♦ **inheritance:** possessions given to heirs.
- ♦ **possession:** something purchased, an acquisition.
- ♦ **redemption:** setting slaves of sin free to live for God.
- ♦ **praise:** commendation, a commendable thing, laudation.
- ♦ **glory:** the evidence of God's wonderful work or character, honor.

➤5. Look back through this list of words. Circle one that you would like to understand or experience more fully.

### Looking Through the Scripture to God

 **Now pause to pray.**
- Thank God for the spiritual blessings He has given you.
- Ask the Lord to give you understanding about your salvation.
- Ask the Lord to affirm to you the true nature of your relationship with Him. Ask Him to bring you to a place of assurance based on His guarantee.
- Ask the Lord to give you understanding about the work of the Holy Spirit in your salvation.
- Close your prayer time by praying Ephesians 1:17-19 and 3:16-19 (on your bookmark) for yourself and your minichurch.

**OUR SPIRITUAL BLESSINGS**
- He included us in Christ.
- He marked us in Christ with the Holy Spirit.
- He guaranteed our inheritance.

## PART 2: WHO IS THE SPIRIT?

**Ephesians 1:13-14**

"Having believed, you were marked in him with a seal, the promised Holy Spirit, who is a deposit guaranteeing our inheritance until the redemption of those who are God's possession."

➤6. Read again Ephesians 1:13-14 in the margin. Circle words that tell you something about who or what the Holy Spirit is.

**The Holy Spirit Is the One "Promised."** Paul told us that the Holy Spirit was the One promised to believers. Peter, in his sermon on the Day of Pentecost, also described the Holy Spirit as the gift of God promised to all who repent and turn to Christ for salvation:

> "Repent and be baptized, every one of you, in the name of Jesus Christ for the forgiveness of your sins. And you will receive the gift of the Holy Spirit. The promise is for you and your children and for all who are far off—for all whom the Lord our God will call" (Acts 2:38-39).

Let's look at the words of Jesus to see what He had to say about this One who was to come.

➤7. As you read the following statements from Jesus, match them with the statements in the left margin that describe the Holy Spirit. Write the letter beside the verse. Some verses will have more than one letter. Some letters will apply to more than one verse.

a. He is a Counselor.

b. He is truth.

c. He will guide you to all truth.

d. He will teach you.

e. He will help you know what your inheritance is (what belongs to you).

f. He testifies about Christ.

g. He will speak to you words from the Father.

h. He will remind you of what Jesus has said.

i. He will tell you what is to come.

j. He will live in you.

k. He will be with you forever.

1. _____ John 14:15-17—"If you love me, you will obey what I command. And I will ask the Father, and he will give you another Counselor to be with you forever—the Spirit of truth. . . . you know him, for he lives with you and will be in you."

2. _____ John 14:26—"The Counselor, the Holy Spirit, whom the Father will send in my name, will teach you all things and will remind you of everything I have said to you."

3. _____ John 15:26-27—"When the Counselor comes, whom I will send to you from the Father, the Spirit of truth who goes out from the Father, he will testify about me."

4. _____ John 16:13-15—"When he, the Spirit of truth, comes, he will guide you into all truth. He will not speak on his own; he will speak only what he hears, and he will tell you what is yet to come. He will bring glory to me by taking from what is mine and making it known to you. All that belongs to the Father is mine. That is why I said the Spirit will take from what is mine and make it known to you."

(Answers: 1–a, b, j, k; 2–a, d, h; 3–a, b, f; 4–b, c, e, g, i)

Jesus told His disciples what they could expect the Holy Spirit to do. This Counselor and Teacher is the One promised to believers.

**The Holy Spirit Is the Seal of God's Ownership.** Have you ever written your name in a book so people will know it's yours? Have you ever engraved your name or an ID number on property in your home so you can identify it if it's ever stolen? We mark items this way in order to claim ownership. In a similar way, when you believe in Christ, God marks you with the seal of the Holy Spirit. In 2 Corinthians 1:21-22, Paul explained that God "anointed us, set his seal of ownership on us, and put his Spirit in our hearts as a deposit, guaranteeing what is to come." You belong to God. God wants you and others to know it. When people see the Holy Spirit in your life, they'll know you are God's child.

♦ **seal:** stamp with a signet or private mark for security or showing ownership.

_____

_____

_____

_____

➤8. In the margin, in your own words, describe what the "seal" of the Holy Spirit means.

♦ **deposit:** earnest, a pledge given in advance as security for the rest.

**2 Corinthians 5:4-5**
"While we are in this tent, we groan and are burdened, because we do not wish to be unclothed but to be clothed with our heavenly dwelling, so that what is mortal may be swallowed up by life. Now it is God who has made us for this very purpose and has given us the Spirit as a deposit, guaranteeing what is to come."

**The Holy Spirit Is God's "Deposit" and "Guarantee."** If you were to sign a contract to buy a house, you would be required to give a sum of money as a deposit. This is a way of guaranteeing you will follow through on your agreement. Though human beings may fail to keep their agreements (even when they lose their deposit), God is faithful and will keep all His promises. When you believe in Christ, God gives "the Spirit as a deposit, guaranteeing what is to come" (2 Cor. 5:5). He guarantees your inheritance and redemption (Eph. 1:14). He guarantees your heavenly dwelling in eternity, and He guarantees all that He has promised about your future with Him in eternity (2 Cor. 5:4-5). "But," you may ask, "how would I know that I have the deposit of the Holy Spirit?"

➤9. **Read the following scriptures, and answer the questions that follow.**

**1 Corinthians 3:16**—"Don't you know that you yourselves are God's temple and that God's Spirit lives in you?"

**1 Corinthians 6:19-20**—"Do you not know that your body is a temple of the Holy Spirit, who is in you, whom you have received from God? You are not your own; you were bought at a price. Therefore honor God with your body."

**Galatians 4:6-7**—"Because you are sons, God sent the Spirit of his Son into our hearts, the Spirit who calls out, 'Abba, Father.' So you are no longer a slave, but a son; and since you are a son, God has made you also an heir."

➤10. **Where does the Holy Spirit live?**

_____

➤11. **With the Holy Spirit in your heart, what kind of relationship do you have with God? Check all that apply.**
   ❏ a. I'm a slave.   ❏ b. I'm a son (child).   ❏ c. I'm an heir.

**2 Corinthians 3:16-18**—"Whenever anyone turns to the Lord, the veil is taken away. Now the Lord is the Spirit, and where the Spirit of the Lord is, there is freedom. And we, who with unveiled faces all reflect the Lord's glory, are being transformed into his likeness with ever-increasing glory, which comes from the Lord, who is the Spirit."

**Romans 8:16**—"The Spirit himself testifies with our spirit that we are God's children."

**1 John 3:24**—"Those who obey his commands live in him, and he in them. And this is how we know that he lives in us: We know it by the Spirit he gave us."

➤12. **As you are changed to look like the Lord, what do you reflect in increasing amounts?**

_____

➤13. **How would you know that you have God's deposit and guarantee—His Holy Spirit? Check <u>one or more</u> correct responses.**
   ❏ a. I can't know. I just have to guess.
   ❏ b. I can know because the Spirit works to help me look like Jesus Christ.
   ❏ c. I can know because the Spirit witnesses to my spirit that He is in me.

When you believe in Christ, the Holy Spirit comes to live in you. He makes your body His temple. With the Spirit of Christ in you, you show the family resemblance as a son or child of God (12b). You also are entitled to all that belongs to Christ because you are an heir (10c)—you have an inheritance! As the Holy Spirit is allowed to do His work, you will become more and more like Christ. The more you look like

Christ, the more you reflect His glory. You can know of His presence because He will bear witness to you (12c).

 Think about the evidence in your life that the Spirit lives there. Does your life reflect God's likeness and glory? Take some time to pray to the Lord about the work of His Spirit in you. Give Him permission to continue His work. Ask Him to continue revealing more and more of Himself through your life.

### PART 3: GOD THE SPIRIT'S ACTIONS

As we have studied already, God the Father planned your salvation. God the Son (Jesus Christ) carried out the plan. God the Spirit has guaranteed that the plan will be completed. God has prepared the way for your salvation, but you must experience it. In his letter to the believers at Rome, Paul described the process:

"'Everyone who calls on the name of the Lord will be saved.'"
"How, then, can they call on the one they have not believed in? And how can they believe in the one of whom they have not heard? And how can they hear without someone preaching to them?" (Rom. 10:13-14).

For a person to call on the name of the Lord and be saved, he must believe. To believe, he must hear and understand. God calls believers to tell others about the good news (the gospel). But the Holy Spirit must be involved to do two things:
1. The Holy Spirit opens our minds to understand the truth of the gospel.
2. The Holy Spirit opens our hearts to believe the gospel.

When the Holy Spirit has done His work, we can believe and call on the name of the Lord for salvation. Without the work of the Holy Spirit, a person would never come to faith in Christ.

▶14. **Place the following items involved in salvation in the correct order. Mark the first item "1" through the last item "7."**
_____ a. Jesus provided for salvation.
_____ b. The person calls on Christ to save him or her.
_____ c. The Holy Spirit helps the person understand the truth.
_____ d. Someone tells the good news to the person.
_____ e. The person believes (or trusts) Christ.
_____ f. The Holy Spirit opens the person's heart to want to believe.
_____ g. Jesus saves the person.
(Answers: 1-a; 2-d; 3-c; 4-f; 5-e; 6-b; 7-g)

**The Gospel.** The gospel is the good news about the salvation God provides through Christ. Paul summarized the message to the church at Corinth.

▶15. **Read 1 Corinthians 15:1-4 in the margin. Underline the experiences in the life of Christ that are of "first importance."**

Christ died for our sins. He was buried. He was raised from the dead the third day, just as God had said He would be. Paul preached this message to the people of Corinth. Knowing the facts of the life of Christ, however, was not enough for salvation. They had to understand and believe the message. They had to place their faith in the Lord. How can human beings understand how Christ's death, burial, and resurrection can provide salvation? Only God can help us understand this truth.

**Understanding the Gospel.** Once a person hears the message of the gospel, the Holy Spirit is the One who brings understanding. Paul said, "The man without the Spirit does not accept the things that come from the Spirit of God, for they are foolishness

---

♦ **truth:** that which is true, ultimate reality.

♦ **gospel:** a good message, good news.

♦ **salvation:** rescue, safety, deliverance from the eternal penalty of death for sin.

♦ **believe:** to have faith in, upon, or with respect to; to entrust one's spiritual well-being to Christ, commit, trust.

**1 Corinthians 15:1-4**

"I want to remind you of the gospel I preached to you, which you received and on which you have taken your stand. By this gospel you are saved, if you hold firmly to the word I preached to you. Otherwise, you have believed in vain.

"For what I received I passed on to you as of first importance: that Christ died for our sins according to the Scriptures, that he was buried, that he was raised on the third day according to the Scriptures."

to him, and he cannot understand them, because they are spiritually discerned" (1 Cor. 2:14). Paul wrote to the Corinthians that God has made known "a wisdom that has been hidden and that God destined for our glory before time began," and that "God has revealed it to us <u>by his Spirit</u>" (1 Cor. 2:7, 10). Paul reminded these New Testament Christians that "none of the rulers of this age understood it, for if they had, they would not have crucified the Lord of glory" (1 Cor. 2:8).

How, then, can we come to understand God's thoughts? Paul answered this question specifically for the Corinthians: "We have not received the spirit of the world but the Spirit who is from God, that we may <u>understand</u> what God has freely given us" (1 Cor. 2:12). The Holy Spirit opens our minds to understand "the word of truth"— the gospel of our salvation.

➤ **16. How do you come to understand the gospel? Check one.**
  ❑ a. I use my human reasoning, and it just makes sense.
  ❑ b. The Holy Spirit opens my mind to understand.
  ❑ c. A really smart preacher explains it to me, and it makes sense.

The Holy Spirit is the only One who can help you understand, even though a smart preacher may help explain the message. But understanding is still short of believing and trusting. The Holy Spirit helps there too.

**Believing the Gospel.** It's one thing to know and understand the gospel. It's another to believe it and receive the gift of salvation. Thus Paul wrote to these Christians, "<u>Having believed</u>, you were marked in him with a seal, the promised Holy Spirit" (Eph. 1:13).

When Paul and his missionary team arrived in Philippi, they found a group of women who had gathered for prayer. Paul and his companions began to present the gospel. One of these ladies was Lydia, a businesswoman who manufactured and sold purple cloth. Though she worshiped God, she had not yet come to know Christ as her personal Savior. As Paul explained the gospel, "<u>the Lord opened her heart to respond</u> to Paul's message" (Acts 16:14).

➤ **17. Who opened Lydia's heart to believe and respond to Paul's message? Check the correct response.**
  ❑ a. Paul opened her heart to respond.
  ❑ b. Lydia did it all by herself. She didn't need any help.
  ❑ c. The Lord opened her heart to respond.

God did it! This is a direct reference to the work of the Holy Spirit as He enables a person to respond and believe in the death, burial, and resurrection of Jesus Christ. True, we respond with our own understanding and will, but the fact remains that "no one can say, 'Jesus is Lord,' except by the Holy Spirit" (1 Cor. 12:3). The best news in this truth is that a person doesn't have to do it alone. God will help bring understanding and belief.

**I Was Born Again by the Spirit.** When I (Gene) accepted Jesus Christ as my personal Savior at age 16, I didn't experience anything unusual—except that I knew I was born again. I knew the Holy Spirit of Christ had come to dwell in my heart. I knew my sins were forgiven. Though it took some time and lots of good teaching to understand what had happened, I knew I was God's child. I remember it so well. It was on July 7, 1948.

It all began while I was working out in the barnyard on our farm in Indiana. Two of my best friends—twin brothers—had become Christians and had told me about their decision. I listened, but I refused to accept Christ myself. *There are too many exciting things to do as a non-Christian*, I thought.

I spent many days—and nights—in mental arguments with the Holy Spirit. But that day I remember throwing down the shovel I had in my hands and going into the house. I took one look at my mother, and she knew why I had come to her side. She had witnessed my struggle with God. We went to my bedroom upstairs and knelt by my bed. I invited Jesus Christ into my life to be my Savior. That day I was spiritually baptized into the Body of Christ by the Holy Spirit, who came to live in my heart.

And so it is with everyone who truly believes the gospel message. Psychological experiences may vary, but it's the same event. We are born again by the Spirit of God. It involves the same factors Jesus explained to Nicodemus when he inquired about the new birth:

> "'I tell you the truth, no one can enter the kingdom of God unless he is born of water and the Spirit. Flesh gives birth to flesh, but <u>the Spirit gives birth to spirit.</u> . . . The wind blows wherever it pleases. You hear its sound, but you cannot tell where it comes from or where it is going. So it is with everyone born of the Spirit'" (John 3:5-6, 8).

**We are born again by the Spirit of God.**

►18. Take a moment to reflect on the time when you were "born again." Your experience was probably different from the one described above. God deals with each of us uniquely. Write a few notes in the margin about what you experienced or what you remember.

Thank the Lord for what He has done for you through His Spirit. Since so many others need to hear, understand, and believe the gospel, ask the Lord to give you boldness to present the message to at least one other person. Ask Him to help you understand:

- whom to present this message to (He knows those who may be ready to receive the message).
- when to present the message (He knows the right timing).
- how to present the message (He will give you the right words to say).

**Redeemed**
by Fanny J. Crosby

Redeemed—how I love to proclaim it!
Redeemed by the blood of the Lamb;
Redeemed through His infinite mercy,
His child, and forever, I am.

OUR SPIRITUAL BLESSINGS

PART 1

- He chose us.
- He predestined us to be adopted as His children.
- He has freely given us His grace.

PART 2

- He redeemed us.
- He provided forgiveness for our sins.
- He lavished grace on us with all wisdom and understanding.
- He made known to us the mystery of His will.

PART 3

- He included us in Christ.
- He marked us in Christ with the Holy Spirit.
- He guaranteed our inheritance.

## PART 4: RESPONDING TO GOD

As we conclude our study of this three-part "hymn," we want to review the spiritual blessings described in Ephesians 1:3-14.

▶19. **Read through the list to the left, and draw a star beside one or two that have been especially meaningful to you during our study.**

Paul wrote a refrain for this hymn that he repeated three times.

▶20. **Can you remember the two key words that describe the results God desires from our lives? Write them below.**

P _____    and   G _____

If you need help remembering, read the hymn again in Ephesians 1:3-14. In His Sermon on the Mount, Jesus said something about our lives bringing praise to our heavenly Father. He said,

> "You are the light of the world. A city on a hill cannot be hidden. Neither do people light a lamp and put it under a bowl. Instead they put it on its stand, and it gives light to everyone in the house. In the same way, let your light shine before men, that they may see your good deeds and praise your Father in heaven" (Matt. 5:14-16).

▶21. **Go back and underline the command Jesus gave us in the last part of the statement. Then answer the following questions.**

1. What are you to do with the light of Christ that is in you?

_____

2. When people see God's goodness flowing from your life, how will they respond?

_____

The best way for your life to bring praise and glory to the Father is for you to let His Spirit live and shine through you. His Spirit is in you. God is going to be working in your life to conform you to the image of His Son. He can and will use all things (both bad and good experiences) to accomplish this work if you will let Him. Paul said,

> "We know that in all things God works for the good of those who love him, who have been called according to his purpose. For those God foreknew he also predestined to be conformed to the likeness of his Son, that he might be the firstborn among many brothers" (Rom. 8:28-29).

Have you ever claimed the first part of that passage as a promise without knowing what God has in mind? He's going to use every circumstance in your life to shape you to look like Christ. A well-known sculptor once was asked, "How can you carve such a beautiful angel out of that lump of marble?" He responded, "There's an angel in there, and I just chip away everything that isn't angel."

That's what God is doing with your life. He has placed the Spirit of Christ in you. He's trying to chip away all that remains of your sinful human nature. Then when people see your life, they will see the glory of Christ revealed in you. Sometimes, however, as God chips something away, we may pick it back up and hold onto it. God must grieve when we do that.

He knows He will only have to chip us again until we let it go.

**Galatians 5:16-18**

"Live by the Spirit, and you will not gratify the desires of the sinful nature. For the sinful nature desires what is contrary to the Spirit, and the Spirit what is contrary to the sinful nature. They are in conflict with each other, so that you do not do what you want. But if you are led by the Spirit, you are not under law."

**Galatians 5:19-21**

"The acts of the sinful nature are obvious: sexual immorality, impurity and debauchery; idolatry and witchcraft; hatred, discord, jealousy, fits of rage, selfish ambition, dissensions, factions and envy; drunkenness, orgies, and the like. I warn you, as I did before, that those who live like this will not inherit the kingdom of God."

**Galatians 5:22-25**

"But the fruit of the Spirit is love, joy, peace, patience, kindness, goodness, faithfulness, gentleness and self-control. Against such things there is no law. Those who belong to Christ Jesus have crucified the sinful nature with its passions and desires. Since we live by the Spirit, let us keep in step with the Spirit."

**Revive Us Again**
by William P. Mackay

➤22. **Which of the following best describes how God can get the greatest glory from your life? Check your response.**
   ❏ a. When I do my human best, others will see what a good person I am, and I can tell them about God.
   ❏ b. When I flee from evil and allow Christ to live in me, others will see Christ in me and glorify my heavenly Father.

Paul described our need to live by the Spirit in his letter to the Galatians.

➤23. **Read Galatians 5:16-18 in the margin. How can you avoid gratifying the desires of your sinful nature?**

_____

➤24. **Read Galatians 5:19-21 in the margin, and circle the acts of the sinful nature.**

➤25. **Read Galatians 5:22-25 in the margin, and circle the fruit of the Spirit.**

➤26. **If God were to use these two lists to evaluate your life, which of the following would be most true of you? Check your response.**
   ❏ a. God's Spirit is in control, and I see His fruit in my life. Love, joy, peace, patience, kindness, goodness, faithfulness, gentleness, and self-control are showing in my life. I praise You, Father.
   ❏ b. My life is a battle. Often the Spirit's fruit shows, but at other times I give evidence that my sinful nature is too strong. Lord, help me live under the Spirit's control.
   ❏ c. My sinful nature is almost always in control. I see little or no fruit of the Spirit in my life. Lord, I need to die to sin, but I need Your help.

Since God has lavished His blessings on us, how should we live? We are eternally to be "the praise of his glory." We should live worthy of this calling right now. "Since we live by the Spirit, let us keep in step with the Spirit" (Gal. 5:25). This means we will reflect the fruit of the Spirit (Gal. 5:22).

 **Take a moment as we conclude this lesson to talk to the Lord about what you see in your life. Ask Him to show you how to let the Spirit fill and control your life more completely. Then take time to express your thanks and praise to Him. You may want to read or sing the following hymn to Him in closing:**

We praise thee, O God, for the Son of Thy love,
For Jesus who died and is now gone above

[Refrain]
Hallelujah! Thine the glory, Hallelujah! Amen;
Hallelujah! Thine the glory; Revive us again.

We praise thee, O God, for Thy Spirit of light,
Who has shown us our Saviour and scattered our night.

All glory and praise to the Lamb that was slain,
Who has borne all our sins and has cleansed every stain.

Revive us again; fill each heart with Thy love;
May each soul be rekindled with fire from above.

# MINICHURCH MEETING 4

**BEFORE THE MEETING**

❑ 1. Turn to "Preparing for Your Minichurch Meeting" on page 143. Use it as a guide to get ready for this meeting. Check the box above after you have prepared.

❑ 2. Unless God should direct otherwise, your minichurch leader will be using the following outline to guide your meeting. You may want to look over the questions and activities so you will be better prepared to participate.

**DURING THE MEETING**

❖ **Opening Prayer**

❖ **Singing Together**

Consider singing "Redeemed, How I Love to Proclaim It," "Revive Us Again," or "Sweet, Sweet Spirit" together with other choruses and hymns.

❖ **Building Relationships**

1. Married people: Tell something funny, interesting, or unusual that happened related to your engagement, wedding, or honeymoon.

2. Singles: Tell one of your favorite memories from school days (elementary, high school, or college).

3. (in fours or sixes) What's one of your greatest desires for your immediate family? (This may relate to a marriage partner, parent, child, brother, sister, or someone else who lives in your home.)

❖ **Praying for One Another** (in fours or sixes)

Pray for the other individuals in your group. Pray specifically for their family needs, relationships, or desires. Ask God to develop godly families that will enrich your lives and bring Him glory.

❖ **Interacting with the Scriptures** (in fours or sixes)

1. What verse or passage of Scripture has been most meaningful or challenging to you this week? How has God used it to speak to you? What significant actions have you taken this week because of something God revealed through His Word?

2. (p. 46) Volunteers: Recite the memory verse you learned this week, and explain any special meaning you gained from it.

3. (p. 46, #5) What word or phrase from Ephesians 1:13-14 have you come to better understand or experience this week? Describe your understanding or experience.

❖ **Reviewing the Lesson**

1. (pp. 47-48) What facts do you know about the Holy Spirit and His work with believers?

2. What did Paul mean when he said the Holy Spirit is a "seal" and a "deposit"?

3. (p. 49, #14) How does God work to bring a person to faith in His Son?

4. (pp. 49-50) What is the gospel? How is the Holy Spirit involved in a person's believing the gospel?

❖ **Applying the Truths to Life**

1. (p. 49) How have you experienced the work of the Holy Spirit in your life? What are some evidences that He lives in your life?

2. (p. 51, #18) Volunteers who have not already done so: Tell of your experience of being born again. What scriptures and/or people were involved in pointing you to Jesus?

3. (p. 52, #19) What two spiritual blessings have been especially meaningful to you, and why?

4. Describe a person you know who lets the light of Jesus shine through his or her life.

5. (p. 53, #22) How does God get the greatest glory from your life?

6. (p. 53) What are the acts of the sinful nature? What is the fruit of the Spirit? How can these things be helpful indicators of the Spirit's working in your life?

❖ **Praying for One Another** (in fours or sixes)

Allow members to respond to the following questions. (You may want to write some notes to yourself so you can continue praying for one another during the week.) Then pray for one another's spiritual growth and well-being.

1. What do you sense is your greatest spiritual need right now?

2. How can we pray for you?

❖ **Ministering to One Another**

What needs (if any) of members have you become aware of during this meeting or during this week that the Body needs to care for? What can we do to meet the needs or to help connect the person with those who can help? Are there things we need to do today or this week to help?

❖ **Reaching Out to Others**

Are there people in your circles of influence who need a saving relationship with Jesus Christ and for whom God seems to be giving you a special burden? What can we pray or do to help you carry that burden?

❖ **Closing Prayer**

❖ **Optional: "Breaking Bread" Together**

# LESSON 5
# LEARNING TO KNOW GOD BETTER

**Experiencing God**

**Hagar's Story**

"Sarai mistreated Hagar; so she fled from her.

"The angel of the LORD found Hagar near a spring in the desert . . . . And he said, 'Hagar, servant of Sarai, where have you come from, and where are you going?'

"'I'm running away from my mistress Sarai,' she answered.

"Then the angel of the LORD told her, 'Go back to your mistress and submit to her.' The angel added, 'I will so increase your descendants that they will be too numerous to count.'

"The angel of the LORD also said to her: 'You are now with child and you will have a son. You shall name him Ishmael, for the LORD has heard of your misery.' . . .

"She gave this name to the LORD who spoke to her: 'You are the God who sees me,' for she said, 'I have now seen the One who sees me'" (Gen. 16:6-11, 13).

(Claude's story) One of my favorite names for God is found in Genesis 16:13. Hagar felt used and abused. She was pregnant, homeless, helpless, and alone. She had reached a point of despair. Then she encountered God. Essentially God said, "I know what you are going through. I care about you, and I'm going to take care of you." Hagar gave God a new name that day: "the God who sees me."

One Saturday morning, I decided to find a place to walk and talk with the Lord. On my way down Highway 231, I took several unplanned turns and wound up at a park beside the river. I began walking and praying. Soon I heard footsteps behind me. I turned and saw a tall, husky man with dirty work clothes coming in my direction. My first emotion was fear. Then I heard Steve speak, and I realized this was a troubled man.

Steve told me that his father had died just before Christmas. His mother had terminal cancer; and due to lack of insurance, Steve was working three jobs trying to cover the medical bills. One of his jobs involved picking up repossessed cars with his wrecker service. He showed me his right hand where he had been shot two weeks before by an angry car owner. He went on to describe his concern for his 17-year-old son, who was getting into trouble. Steve was distressed because he was not home to be the dad his son needed. Then he told me how his wife and younger son had been killed by a drunk driver eight years before, leaving no mother at home to help.

I asked Steve about his relationship with the Lord. When he was 19, he was drafted to go to Vietnam. In the process of "experiencing life" before leaving, he wound up in the county jail. While he was there, a person came by and told him about Jesus Christ, and Steve trusted Christ as his personal Lord and Savior. Steve went on to tell me about his experience in Vietnam. He became a prisoner of war. He said, "That's the reason I wear my hair long like this. They cut off my ears, and I don't want to offend people." I asked Steve about his current walk with the Lord. He said, "Every morning I wake up and fall on my knees and ask God to help me make it through one more day. Then when I get home at night, I fall on my knees and thank God for taking me through one more day."

I realized that God was up to something. Here was a child of God who had reached a point of despair. I was not there by accident. All my random turns that morning had been directed by God to put me together with Steve. The God who sees had a child who was desperately in need of hope and help. God needed a person to minister to Steve and remind him that he had not been forgotten. I told Steve the story of Hagar and about the God who sees. I said, "Steve, your heavenly Father knows what you're going through. He cares about you, and He's going to take care of you."

After a time of discussion and prayer, an excitement and joy filled Steve's voice. He was overwhelmed to know that God cared enough to pay special attention to him at this crisis time in his life. Steve and I both had encountered the God who sees. God had revealed Himself to us by experience.

## Part 1: Interacting with the Scriptures

**Read or Listen to:**
- ❑ Ephesians 1–6
- ❑ Ephesians 1–3
- ❑ Ephesians 1:1-23

### Reading / Hearing God's Word

➤1. Select one of the reading (or listening) options in the margin. Using your Bible, read or listen to the passage of Scripture. As you begin, ask God to speak to you through His Word. Watch for one verse or idea that's especially meaningful to you today. Once you finish reading, check the box indicating the passage you read.

### Meditating on God's Word

**Meaningful Verse or Idea**

_____

_____

_____

➤2. In the margin, write a brief summary of the meaningful verse or idea you just identified. Take time today to reflect on its meaning.

### Memorizing God's Word

➤3. Select and tear out a new Scripture memory card from the back of your book, or continue reviewing the one you started learning earlier. For a new verse, use the tips for memorizing Scripture on your bookmark.

### Understanding God's Word

**Ephesians 1:15-17**

"For this reason, ever since I heard about your faith in the Lord Jesus and your love for all the saints, I have not stopped giving thanks for you, remembering you in my prayers. I keep asking that the God of our Lord Jesus Christ, the glorious Father, may give you the Spirit of wisdom and revelation, so that you may know him better."

➤4. Read again the focal passage for this week's lesson (Eph. 1:15-17) in the margin. Underline any key phrases or ideas that seem especially meaningful to you. Then read the brief definitions of key words below. This will prepare you for the remainder of this week's study.

- ♦ **faith:** constancy in relationship to Christ, loyalty to Christ, continuing to trust in Christ, fidelity.
- ♦ **love:** [*agape*] godly affection, benevolence, seeking the very best for another unconditionally.
- ♦ **saints:** sacred ones, ones set apart as holy, set apart for God.
- ♦ **Lord:** supreme in authority, controller, Master.
- ♦ **Christ:** the Messiah, anointed One.
- ♦ **glorious:** full of glory, dignified, honorable, praiseworthy.
- ♦ **Spirit:** the divine Holy Spirit of God.
- ♦ **wisdom:** understanding the true nature of things.
- ♦ **revelation:** illumination, manifestation, appearing, uncovering.
- ♦ **know:** fully discern, to become fully acquainted with, to gain intimate and experiential knowledge of.

➤5. Look back through this list of words. Circle one that you would like to understand or experience more fully.

### Looking through the Scripture to God

 Now pause to pray. Approach God with the respect shown by Paul by realizing that He is God, Lord, Messiah, glorious, and your heavenly Father.

- Reflect on your own faith and love for other believers. Talk to the Lord about your desires to be more faithful and loving.
- Give thanks to the Lord for other believers who have been an encouragement and example to your life.
- Ask the Lord to grant a Spirit of wisdom and revelation to your minichurch and to your larger congregation so that you may know Him better as you experience God working in and through your lives.
- Close by praying Ephesians 1:17-19 and 3:16-19 (on your bookmark) for yourself and your minichurch.

## PART 2: PRAYING FOR THE SAINTS

When Paul said, "For this reason," he was connecting what he had just said in verses 3-14 with what he was about to say. God had blessed these saints "with every spiritual blessing." God had redeemed them and placed His Holy Spirit in them so their lives would bring praise and glory to Him. When Paul heard about the faith of these saints and the quality of godly love they had for other believers, he must have thought, *That's it!* God's work was being perfected in their lives. They were bringing glory and praise to the Lord. So "for this reason," Paul was filled with thanksgiving to the Lord for what He had done in these believers. God had done a glorious work, and their lives brought Him glory.

➤ 6. **If a godly man like Paul heard about the faith of your church and the love you demonstrate through caring actions toward all other believers, how do you think he would respond to the Lord? Check a possible response or write your own.**

❑ a. Lord, You've done a wonderful work in these people. They bring glory and praise to You by their faith and loving service to the saints.

❑ b. Lord, You've begun a good work in these people. However, they're still rather shallow in their faith and loving actions toward the rest of the saints.

❑ c. Lord, these people are selfish and self-centered. They claim You've done a work of grace in their lives, but I don't see Your work very clearly.

❑ d. Other: _____

---

### PAUL'S PRAYERS FOR OTHERS

#### Colossians 1:9-10

"Since the day we heard about you, we have not stopped praying for you and asking God to fill you with the knowledge of his will through all spiritual wisdom and understanding And we pray this in order that you may live a life worthy of the Lord and may please him in every way: bearing fruit in every good work, growing in the knowledge of God" (Col. 1:9-10).

#### Philippians 1:9-11

"This is my prayer: that your love may abound more and more in knowledge and depth of insight, so that you may be able to discern what is best and may be pure and blameless until the day of Christ, filled with the fruit of righteousness that comes through Jesus Christ—to the glory and praise of God."

Paul probably would have checked *a* for these Gentile Christians. But he knew that the Christian life is a lifelong process of growing in Christlikeness. His concern was that they know God better. They had been converted to Christ out of a pagan lifestyle that was totally selfish and sinful. They still needed to grow. Paul began to pray for these believers. He asked that God would reveal Himself to them in such a way that they would come to know Him better. Paul was a real "prayer warrior." He went to spiritual battle for other believers in his prayers for them. How would you feel if someone like Paul were praying for you?

No matter how you responded to the question above, God wants to help your church grow into maturity. Praying for your church and other believers is a beginning place for new growth. Paul frequently told churches he was praying for them. He also frequently asked them to pray for him. He knew that prayers offered in the throne room of the universe have great power. Later in this letter he said, "Pray in the Spirit on all occasions with all kinds of prayers and requests. With this in mind, be alert and always keep on praying for all the saints" (Eph. 6:18).

 **Take time right now to pray for your church. Pray that God would increase the people's faith, that He would enable you to love other saints in a way that would honor Him, and that He would reveal Himself to your church in a way that you will come to know Him better. Using your bookmark, pray Ephesians 3:16-19 for your church. Use Paul's prayers in the margin also. As you pray, mention specific people and situations.**

We all need to pray for each other and for all the saints. However, God seems to give some people a special calling to devote themselves more fully to prayer. We sometimes call these people "prayer warriors." Carrying out a ministry of intercession for others is a high calling.

**Romans 8:26-27**

"The Spirit helps us in our weakness. We do not know what we ought to pray for, but the Spirit himself intercedes for us with groans that words cannot express. And . . . the Spirit intercedes for the saints in accordance with God's will."

**Romans 8:34**

"Christ Jesus . . . is at the right hand of God and is also interceding for us."

**Hebrews 7:25**

"Therefore he [Christ] is able to save completely those who come to God through him, because he always lives to intercede for them."

➤ 7. Read the scriptures in the margin, and answer these questions.

1. What is our one great weakness? (Rom. 8:26)

_____

2. Who intercedes (prays—asking on our behalf) for us according to God's will? (Rom. 8:27)

_____

3. Who is now at the right hand of God, interceding for us? (Rom. 8:34)

_____

4. According to Hebrews 7:25, what is Christ always living to do for us?

_____

If God calls you to a hidden ministry of intercession, you're in good company. He has given the same calling to His Holy Spirit and to Christ Jesus, His Son. The Spirit helps us when we don't know what to pray. He prays with us and for us according to God's will. Jesus lives to pray for us—intercession is His life.

 8. **Ask God about what role He would have you play in praying for others. Be open in the coming days to hearing God's call to greater intercession for others. He may call you to . . .**
- devote yourself and much of your time to being a prayer warrior for others.
- give extended periods of time to praying for specific needs when they arise.
- take time regularly to pray for and even with other believers.

Paul was a tentmaker by trade. He earned his own living so he could preach the gospel "free of charge" (1 Cor. 9:18). He probably spent many hours praying for others while he went about his work. He spent much time traveling from one place to another, walking or by boat, and probably had much time to pray. Then there were times when Paul was in prison and he could again devote long hours and days to intercession.

➤ 9. **When could you take more time to pray for other believers? Check all that apply, and then list some of your own thoughts. I could pray more while . . .**
❏ commuting to work        ❏ working
❏ washing dishes or ironing ❏ mowing grass
❏ jogging, walking, exercising ❏ cleaning house
❏ hunting or fishing        ❏ waiting in a line or office
Others:
❏ _____        ❏ _____
❏ _____        ❏ _____

 Watch for times today and this week to give more time to praying for others. Ask the Lord to impress you to pray at specific times and to guide you in praying for specific needs. Be prepared to describe to your minichurch some of the times or ways God guides you to pray this week.

## PART 3: GROWING IN YOUR KNOWLEDGE OF GOD

Paul was never satisfied with his own spiritual status or that of other Christians. He knew that in many respects, his own Christian life was always in process of becoming—becoming more and more like Jesus. Even toward the end of his life and ministry, he wrote,

> "Not that I have already obtained all this, or have already been made perfect, but I press on to take hold of that for which Christ Jesus took hold of me. Brothers, I do not consider myself yet to have taken hold of it. But one thing I do: Forgetting what is behind and straining toward what is ahead, I press on toward the goal to win the prize for which God has called me heavenward in Christ Jesus" (Phil. 3:12-14).

As long as we live, we need to keep growing toward Christlikeness. Though these Christians were excelling in faith and love, Paul prayed that God might give them "the Spirit of wisdom and revelation, so that you may know him better" (Eph. 1:17). Paul wanted them to continue growing in their knowledge of God.

➤ 10. **What did Paul ask God to give so that these Christians could come to know Him better?**

_____

_____

♦ **Spirit:** the divine Holy Spirit of God.

♦ **wisdom:** understanding the true nature of things.

♦ **revelation:** illumination, manifestation, appearing, uncovering.

♦ **know:** fully discern, to become fully acquainted with, to gain intimate and experiential knowledge of.

### NAMES OF GOD

Author and Perfecter of our faith

Comforter in sorrow

Creator of heaven and earth

God of all comfort

Good Teacher

My Hope

The LORD Will Provide

LORD who makes you holy

Physician

Prince of Peace

Refiner and Purifier

Our Refuge and Strength

My Shepherd

Wonderful Counselor

Paul prayed that God would give them "the Spirit of wisdom and revelation." As you learned in last week's lesson, you cannot understand spiritual truth unless the Holy Spirit reveals it to you. These Christians already had the Holy Spirit. Paul was asking that the Spirit give them godly wisdom. James wrote in his letter, "If any of you lacks wisdom, he should ask God, who gives generously to all without finding fault, and it will be given to him" (James 1:5). Paul also asked that the Holy Spirit would reveal more and more of God to them. If the Spirit would do this, they would get to know God better.

Usually when we think about knowing someone, we think about knowing more information about him. But Paul meant much more here. In Greek (the original language of the New Testament) there's a normal word for _know_ that means a "first awareness" or an "initial and superficial acquaintance with some one or thing." Here, Paul used a different word that means "deep and full knowledge of God." To know God this way means you have an intimate and experiential knowledge of God. You have a firsthand experience of Him as He has revealed Himself to you. We don't need to wait until we're in heaven to begin to experience a deep and full knowledge of God.

➤ 11. **If you've been a Christian very long, you probably have come to know God by experience as He has worked in or around your life. In the margin are some biblical names or descriptions of God. Circle any that describe a way you have come to know Him more fully as He has worked that way in your life. If you can think of other names by which you have experienced Him, write them below.**

_____

_____

_____

What are some ways you can get to know God better? You come to a fuller knowledge of Him as He reveals Himself to you. The first and best place to turn is God's written Word.

**Through the Word of God.** As we read and study the Bible, a profile of God emerges. We see what He's really like. We see that He's holy, that He's all-powerful, that He's all-knowing, that He has the ability to be present everywhere at the same time, that He's eternal, and, perhaps most of all, that He's near and personal. He really cares about me and you! He's a loving heavenly Father.

▶12. **What's one truth you already have learned about God from this study of God's Word in Ephesians?**

_____

If you're to come to know God better, you need to read and study the Bible regularly. As you read, allow the Holy Spirit, who dwells in you, to reveal God to you in new and deeper ways.

**Through Prayer.** As we read in Romans 8:26 (Part 2), our great weakness when we pray is that we don't know what to pray for. Our human mind cannot know the desires and will of God without help. That's where the Holy Spirit comes to our aid. He helps us pray according to God's will. The more we pray about a particular matter and seek God's will or desires, the more the Holy Spirit will begin to reveal God's desires. He will use what we've learned about God and His ways in the Word of God. He will help us come to know God's heart. In prayer we can come to know God more intimately.

Jesus spoke to a "lukewarm church" in Revelation 3:14-22 and extended a special invitation to the believers who wanted to get to know Him better. He said, "Here I am! I stand at the door and knock. If anyone hears my voice and opens the door, I will come in and eat with him, and he with me" (Rev. 3:20). Prayer is not just a religious ritual you go through. It's a relationship with God where you spend time with Him. Even if you're a member of a sick or lukewarm church, you can have intimate fellowship with the Lord. He stands ready to fellowship with you if you will only give Him permission and take the time.

▶13. **So far, you've studied two ways to get to know God better. What are they? Through . . .**

_____ and _____

**Through God's Creation.** I (Gene) enjoy snow skiing for several reasons. But the most exciting part of skiing for me is to stand at the top of a gigantic, snow-covered mountain on a beautiful, sunshiny day. I look out to dozens of other snow-covered peaks. There they stand, jagged and dazzling white against a gloriously blue sky. During those awesome moments, I get chills just thinking that God made all that, and yet He cares about me! That's true. He didn't send His Son to redeem the universe or to save mountains, even snow-covered ones. He sent His Son to redeem me, to make it possible for me to know Him through His Son, Jesus Christ. Through creation, we can see God's glory, majesty, and splendor. Yes, God's creation is one way in which we can come to know Him better. Paul wrote about creation to the Romans:

> "For since the creation of the world God's invisible qualities—his eternal power and divine nature—have been clearly seen, being understood from what has been made, so that men are without excuse" (Rom. 1:20).

➤ 14. In all of God's creation, what parts cause you to stand in awe and amazement at His greatness, creativity, beauty, or splendor?

_____

**1 John 4:11-12**

"Dear friends, since God so loved us, we also ought to love one another. No one has ever seen God; but if we love each other, God lives in us and his love is made complete in us."

**Through Others Who Know Him Well.** God can't be seen since He is spirit. Jesus Christ, who revealed God's love and character, has returned to heaven. How, then, can you know what God is like? John answered that question: When God's "love is made complete in us." (Read 1 John 4:11-12 in the margin.) One of the best ways you can get to know God is by being around others who know Him well and live like Christ in the way they relate to others.

I (Claude) have had the privilege of working with several godly men. When I'm around them I see holiness, purity, and righteousness. I see a servant heart, humility, and love. They're kind and gentle. They express joy and peace. I can tell they've been in God's presence. They seem to know the Lord so intimately, and they love Him dearly. When they pray, I sense they're talking to a close friend. When I'm around them, I want to be more like them. I want to reflect Christ in my life the way I see Christ in their lives.

In writing to the Corinthians, Paul said, "Follow my example, as I follow the example of Christ" (1 Cor. 11:1). He wasn't bragging. He knew that everything of value in his life was because of the work of Christ in him. He was well aware that God had done a wonderful work of grace in his life. He wanted others to experience that Christlikeness just as he had—not because of what he (Paul) had done but because of what Christ had done in him. He knew others could come to know Christ better by seeing Christ in his way of living.

This has profound implications for helping others to come to know God. We all need models of godliness. Perhaps the most profound implication is in the home and falls squarely on the shoulders of those of us who are fathers. The way we live will either help or hinder our children in knowing what a heavenly Father is like. Thank God that He does not lay this burden to represent Him on fathers and mothers exclusively. We all fail. Thus, He has designed the church—the Body of Christ—which should be filled with multiple models of godliness.

The church should have leaders who measure up to the qualities outlined by Paul so clearly in his epistles (1 Tim. 3; Titus 1). But also, there is every member of the Body of Christ. They're to be models of godliness who can balance out our weaknesses, thus giving our children a more well-rounded view of who God is and what He's like. Our goal, then, as individual Christians and as a body of believers, should be to represent God as He really is to all other Christians—and to non-Christians!

➤ 15. Pause to think of the person you know who is most like Christ. Write his or her name on the line below. Thank God for that person. Ask God to help you know Him better and to live more like Christ for others.

_____

## PART 4: RESPONDING TO GOD

**Getting to Know My Wife**

One day while I (Gene) was attending Wheaton Graduate School, Dr. Merrill Tenney was teaching from John 17:3, which reads, "Now this is eternal life: that they may know you, the only true God, and Jesus Christ, whom you have sent." Dr. Tenney pointed out that some people believe Jesus meant that we will spend all eternity coming to know God.

To make this point clear, he used a human illustration. "When you court the person you're going to marry," he said, "you are coming to know that person. Granted, your exposure is superficial. The relationship is just beginning." Then when you get married, Dr. Tenney pointed out, the process of coming to know that person really begins. He then mentioned that at that point he had been married for many years. "Yet," he said, "I am still coming to know my wife and she is still coming to know me. And one of the reasons is that we're both made in the image of God." There is tremendous depth to the human personality.

I realize that my knowledge of my wife, Elaine, just began when we were married. In fact, I must confess that my knowledge of her was quite superficial for a number of years even after we were married. One day we began to discuss more deeply our inner thoughts and feelings. It resulted from a crisis in our relationship. I had been so involved with other people and projects that I was neglecting her. I sat and listened to her pour out her feelings of frustration.

Though it was painful for me to listen, for the first time in our marriage I really began to know Elaine. I saw how committed she had been to me. I had tended to put my study and my work in front of her. I understood her hurts that day. I sensed and identified with her frustration. I was teaching full-time at Dallas Theological Seminary, and I had a heavy schedule planned for the day. However, I made a decision at that moment that was one of the best I've made in my life. I called the seminary, canceled my classes for the day, and just spent time with my wife, listening.

Since that time, I've come to know my wife even better. I realize there are many things I still need to learn. I'm still tempted to become so involved in other things that I neglect her. But things are different now. Even so, I have to work at it every day.

▶16. **Use this marriage illustration to describe your relationship to God based on how much you know Him. Which stage of a marriage relationship do you think best describes where you are in your relationship to God? Check your response and describe why.**

❑ Dating stage          ❑ Fifth anniversary stage

❑ Engagement stage      ❑ Tenth anniversary stage

❑ Honeymoon stage       ❑ Silver (25th) anniversary stage

❑ First Anniversary stage    ❑ Golden (50th) anniversary stage

**Why?**

_____

_____

_____

_____

**Taking Time to Know God.** In our scripture for this lesson, we see that the Ephesian Christians had made a great beginning. They had a strong faith in the Lord Jesus. They also exemplified deep love for their fellow Christians. This was cause for rejoicing. But Paul wrote, "I keep asking that the God of our Lord Jesus Christ, the glorious Father, may give you the Spirit of wisdom and revelation, so that you may know him better" (Eph. 1:17). This is our prayer for you as well. We don't want you to just know about God or about how to get to know Him. We want you to get to know Him better. It's not automatic. Getting to know God better takes time and effort to pursue knowing Him.

### Getting to Know God through His Word

►17. Read through the Psalms in the margin, and circle the words or phrases that tell you something about who God is or what He's like.

### Getting to Know God through Prayer

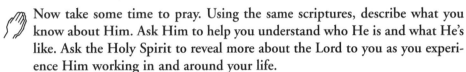

Now take some time to pray. Using the same scriptures, describe what you know about Him. Ask Him to help you understand who He is and what He's like. Ask the Holy Spirit to reveal more about the Lord to you as you experience Him working in and around your life.

18. If time permits before your group session, take another time to walk and talk with the Lord. Follow the instructions in item #18 on page 31. Write below notes about anything you sense God has revealed about Himself during your prayer time with Him. If you don't sense He has revealed anything to you, you may leave this blank.

_____

_____

### Getting to Know God through His Creation

►19. The Bible says, "The heavens declare the glory of God" (Ps. 19:1). For your minichurch session this week, try to bring something that shows you God's glory revealed in creation. It might be something like one of the following:

• a picture from *National Geographic* or another magazine or book
• a photograph of creation that you took on a trip
• a small object of creation like a flower, beautiful rock, a fruit, etc.

Whatever you bring to your group, be prepared to tell how this example of God's creation reveals something about Him to you.

### Getting to Know God Better through Others Who Know Him Well

►20. This is an *optional* assignment and one that may take some time to complete in the next few days or weeks. One way to learn from others who know God well is by reading about their lives through an autobiography, a biography, or a journal. You also may find stories about godly people in a movie or videotape. Check with your church or public library, or visit a local Christian bookstore. Secure a book or video, and see what you can learn about God from the lives of these saints. If you need some suggestions of whom to read about, we've included a list of some godly people in the margin. After reading a book or watching a video, report what you learn to your minichurch.

---

PSALMS ABOUT THE LORD

"The LORD reigns forever; he has established his throne for judgment. He will judge the world in righteousness; he will govern the peoples with justice. The LORD is a refuge for the oppressed, a stronghold in times of trouble" (Ps. 9:7-9).

"Taste and see that the LORD is good; blessed is the man who takes refuge in him" (Ps. 34:8).

"Good and upright is the LORD; therefore he instructs sinners in his ways. He guides the humble in what is right and teaches them his way. All the ways of the LORD are loving and faithful for those who keep the demands of his covenant" (Ps. 25:8-10).

"But you, O Lord, are a compassionate and gracious God, slow to anger, abounding in love and faithfulness" (Ps. 86:15).

William Booth, David Brainerd, John Calvin, William Carey, Amy Carmichael, Fanny J. Crosby, Jim Elliot, Billy Graham, Rees Howells, John Hyde, John Knox, Brother Lawrence, Martin Luther, D. L. Moody, George Muller, Andrew Murray, Bob Pierce, Hannah Whitall Smith, Charles Studd, Hudson Taylor, John Wesley

# MINICHURCH MEETING 5

## BEFORE THE MEETING

❑ 1. Turn to "Preparing for Your Minichurch Meeting" on page 143. Use it as a guide to get ready for this meeting. Check the box above after you have prepared.

❑ 2. Unless God should direct otherwise, your minichurch leader will be using the following outline to guide your meeting. You may want to look over the questions and activities so you will be better prepared to participate.

## DURING THE MEETING

❖ **Opening Prayer**

❖ **Singing Together**

Consider singing "Sweet Hour of Prayer," "More About Jesus," "This Is My Father's World," or "Nearer, My God, to Thee" together with other choruses and hymns.

❖ **Building Relationships**

1. (p. 63, #19) If you brought an object that shows you God's glory revealed in creation, show it to the group and tell what you see of God's glory.

2. (p. 59, #11) Volunteers or all: What's a name of God by which you've come to know Him by experience? Briefly explain the name and your experience.

❖ **Responding to God in Prayer**

Spend some time praising and thanking God for what you've experienced of Him and His character at work in your lives.

❖ **Interacting with the Scriptures** (in fours or sixes)

1. What verse or passage of Scripture has been most meaningful or challenging to you this week? How has God used it to speak to you? What significant actions have you taken this week because of something God revealed through His Word?

2. (p. 56) Volunteers: Recite the memory verse you learned this week, and explain any special meaning you gained from it.

3. (p. 56, #5) What word or phrase from Ephesians 1:15-17 have you come to better understand or experience this week? Describe your understanding or experience.

❖ **Reviewing the Lesson**

1. (p. 57) What specific requests did Paul make as he prayed for others?

2. (p. 59, #10) What does God give to help us know Him better?

3. (pp. 60-61) What are four ways we can get to know God better? Give at least one example of a personal experience of getting to know God in each of these four ways.

❖ **Applying the Truths to Life**

1. Review Hagar's story on page 55, and discuss ways you may have experienced God's love at a time when you were hurting and needed hope. Are any in the group at that point now? If so, let us know so we can comfort and pray with you.

2. What has God been revealing or doing in your heart and mind as you've prayed Paul's prayer for the church from Ephesians 1:17-19 and 3:16-19 each week? What do you sense is your church's (larger congregation's) greatest need in this list of requests on your bookmark?

3. (p. 57) How did you respond to #6, and why? How do we need to pray for our congregation? If this is a pressing concern, pause and pray for your church right now.

4. What difference should it make in your prayer life to know that Jesus and the Holy Spirit are praying for you? Read Hebrews 12:1. Do you think others in heaven may be praying for you also?

5. (p. 58) What, if anything, has God been saying to you about your need to pray more for others?

6. In what ways have you come to know the most about God (Bible, prayer, creation, others)?

7. (p. 62) How did you respond to #16, and why?

8. (p. 63, #20) If you've recently learned something about God from a book, tape, or video about a person who knew God well, tell what you learned.

❖ **Praying for One Another** (in fours or sixes)

Are there names of God by which you want or need to come to know Him experientially? What do you desire most to know about Him? After individuals have spoken, pray for one another. Be specific in your requests. Ask God to take you into experiences where you'll come to know Him better. Thank Him for all He has revealed of Himself through the testimony of others during this meeting.

❖ **Ministering to One Another**

What needs (if any) of members have you become aware of during this meeting that the Body needs to care for? What can we do to meet the needs or to help connect the person with those who can help? Are there things we need to do this week to help?

❖ **Reaching Out to Others**

Are there people in your circles of influence who need a saving relationship with Jesus Christ and for whom God seems to be giving you a special burden? What can we pray or do to help you carry that burden?

❖ **Closing Prayer**

❖ **Optional: "Breaking Bread" Together**

# LESSON 6
# UNDERSTANDING OUR HOPE

"Here's Hope"

In March 1990, I (Claude) read a news release that the True Vine Missionary Baptist Church in Oakland, California, had canceled its planned spring revival services because it didn't have room for all the people. In recent months, 1,250 people had received Christ as Savior, and the congregation needed to find a larger facility. I decided to call the pastor to find out what God was doing.

Pastor Newton Carey described the church's location in one of the poorest areas of California. It was near where the double-decker interstate highway collapsed in the earthquake the year before. He described 15 years of hard and relatively fruitless ministry there. The community was filled with gangs, drugs, prostitution, and other crimes. It was a discouraging place to serve. The previous summer, however, he had picked up a book on prayer and realized his people didn't really know how to pray. "I just taught them right through the book," he said. They began to pray regularly for their church and community. At the same time, the pastor's wife, Sally, started to teach a course in witnessing to some of the members.

A group of church women sensed God wanted to claim a public housing area for Himself, so they marched around it seven times, praying for God to take over. On another occasion, they walked and prayed another seven laps. Two weeks later, the manager of the complex called the church. She said, "When children come home alone after school, they get into all kinds of trouble, and they're vandalizing the property. I was wondering if your church could help by providing activities for the kids." When I talked to the pastor's wife in March, they were ministering to 150-200 children a week. Crime had already begun to drop. Children began to come to Christ. Mothers were coming to Christ and getting off drugs and out of prostitution.

"If you know where I can get hope, you need to tell me, because I don't have any hope."

Someone donated 12,000 copies of an evangelistic New Testament to be given away in the community. The front cover read, "Here's Hope! Jesus Cares for You." On a Saturday, members gathered at the church to distribute the Testaments. As they went from door to door, they would give the gift to the resident. People would see the title and say, "If you know where I can get hope, you need to tell me, because I don't have any hope." That single Saturday, 659 people turned their lives over to Christ. People started to call the church or come by and say, "I hear you have a book about hope, and I need to get a copy." A powerful drug dealer got a copy, and church members led him to the Lord.

God brought hope!

Pastor Carey reported that they were having to turn people away from their Sunday morning service because they didn't have enough room for all the people. In March, they were seeing 20 people a week pray to receive Christ as their Savior. When I called for an update in the summer, the number had grown to 50 a week. God had taken a church in a community with little hope and turned people's eyes toward Him. As God's men and women began to pray and prepare themselves for ministry to the community, God did something that no one could have planned or put on a long-range planning strategy. God brought hope!

Part 1: Interacting with the Scriptures

### Reading/Hearing God's Word

**Read or Listen to:**
- ❑ Ephesians 1–6
- ❑ Ephesians 1–3
- ❑ Ephesians 1:1-23

➤1. Select one of the reading (or listening) options in the margin. Using your Bible, read or listen to the passage of Scripture. As you begin, ask God to speak to you through His Word. Watch for one verse or idea that's especially meaningful to you today. Once you finish reading, check the box indicating the passage you read.

### Meaningful Verse or Idea

_____

_____

_____

### Meditating on God's Word

➤2. In the margin, write a brief summary of the meaningful verse or idea you just identified.

### Memorizing God's Word

➤3. Select and tear out a new Scripture memory card from the back of your book, or continue reviewing one you started learning earlier. For a new verse, use the tips for memorizing Scripture on your bookmark.

### Understanding God's Word

**Ephesians 1:18-19**
"I pray also that the eyes of your heart may be enlightened in order that you may know the hope to which he has called you, the riches of his glorious inheritance in the saints, and his incomparably great power for us who believe."

➤4. Read again the focal passage for this week's lesson (Eph. 1:18-19) in the margin. Underline any key phrases or ideas that seem especially meaningful to you. Then read the brief definitions of key words below. This will prepare you for the remainder of this week's study.

- ♦ **eyes:** (figuratively) your vision, sight, the channel for knowing.
- ♦ **heart:** or mind, deep thought, understanding, the whole of one's inner being.
- ♦ **enlightened:** to shed rays, to illuminate, make to see, instruct.
- ♦ **know:** be aware, have experiential knowledge of, perceive, be sure, understand.
- ♦ **hope:** to anticipate with pleasure, confident expectation.
- ♦ **called:** a summons, an appointment for a particular destiny.
- ♦ **riches:** wealth, abundance, valuable bestowment.
- ♦ **glorious:** full of glory, dignified, honorable, praiseworthy.
- ♦ **inheritance:** possessions given to heirs, eternal blessedness.
- ♦ **saints:** sacred ones, ones set apart as holy, set apart for God, consecrated.
- ♦ **incomparably:** without comparison, beyond the usual, surpassing.
- ♦ **power:** miraculous force, might, strength, ability.
- ♦ **believe:** to have faith in, upon, or with respect to; to entrust one's spiritual well-being to Christ, commit, trust.

➤5. Look back through this list of words. Circle one that you would like to understand or experience more fully.

### Looking through the Scripture to God

 **Now pause to pray.**
- Ask the Lord to open your spiritual eyes to see and understand all the truth He has for you.
- Ask the Lord to firmly establish your hope in your calling to salvation.
- Close by praying Ephesians 1:17-19 and 3:16-19 (on your bookmark) for yourself and your minichurch.

## PART 2: CALLED TO HOPE

Have you ever been on a roller coaster? Imagine for a moment that you didn't know where the ride would end when you climbed aboard and buckled in. It might level out and end its wild journey safely at another point. Or, at some point along the way, it might leave the track and speed off into space—and crash!

Some Christians live as if they're on a spiritual and emotional roller coaster. They're really not sure where they're going to end up in eternity—safely in heaven or eternally separated from God in hell because of some mistake they made along the way.

➤6. **How would you describe your hope in salvation? Check the response closest to your own.**

❑ a. I'm on that "roller coaster" ride. Sometimes I think I'm going to heaven, and other times I'm afraid I'm going to hell.

❑ b. As much as I want to have the hope of salvation, I don't have much hope.

❑ c. Because of God's grace and Christ's shed blood, I have a confident assurance that I'll spend eternity with Him.

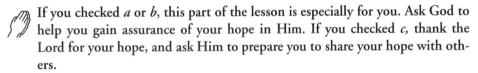 **If you checked *a* or *b*, this part of the lesson is especially for you. Ask God to help you gain assurance of your hope in Him. If you checked *c*, thank the Lord for your hope, and ask Him to prepare you to share your hope with others.**

The Gentile believers Paul was writing to in this letter had difficulty accepting the fact that their salvation was secure in Christ. They probably would have checked *a* or *b* above. Paul was concerned about this, and he continued his prayer for them. He already had prayed that they might come to know God better (Eph. 1:17).

➤7. **Read through the next part of Paul's prayer (Ephesians 1:18-19, in the margin). Look for three things Paul wanted them to know, and underline the words or phrases that describe them.**

Paul wanted them to know "hope," "riches," and "power." He wanted them to come to know these realities by <u>experience</u>. That is our prayer for you too. We'll look at hope and riches this week, and we'll focus on God's power in next week's lesson.

What does the Bible mean by the word *hope*? Hope indicates that we have assurance of salvation and eternal life.

➤8. **Read through the following scriptures, and circle the word *hope* each time it appears.**

**1 Thessalonians 5:8**—"Let us be self-controlled, putting on faith and love as a breastplate, and the hope of salvation as a helmet."

**Titus 1:2**—"A faith and knowledge resting on the hope of eternal life, which God, who does not lie, promised before the beginning of time."

**1 Peter 1:3-4**—"In his great mercy he has given us new birth into a living hope through the resurrection of Jesus Christ from the dead, and into an inheritance that can never perish, spoil or fade—kept in heaven for you."

A Christian can "put on" the hope of salvation like a spiritual helmet to protect his or her mind. For those who believe in Christ, God—"who does not lie"—has promised us eternal life. Our hope is a "living hope" we receive when we're born again. In mercy, God has given us this inheritance in heaven that "can never perish, spoil or fade."

**Ephesians 1:18-19**

"I pray also that the eyes of your heart may be enlightened in order that you may know the hope to which he has called you, the riches of his glorious inheritance in the saints, and his incomparably great power for us who believe."

♦ **hope:** to anticipate with pleasure, confident expectation.

➤9. **What does a Christian hope for? Check the correct response.**

   ❑ a. Both of the following.

   ❑ b. Salvation

   ❑ c. Eternal life

   ❑ d. None of the above.

A Christian's hope is for salvation and the eternal life God has promised. When a Christian truly understands the hope he has in Christ, he has a steadfast sense of security and stability.

➤10. **As you read the following scriptures, underline the words that indicate security or stability. We've underlined one for you.**

   **Hebrews 6:19**—"We have this hope as <u>an anchor</u> for the soul, firm and secure."

   **1 Thessalonians 1:3**—"We continually remember before our God and Father . . . your endurance inspired by hope in our Lord Jesus Christ."

   **Hebrews 10:23**—"Let us hold unswervingly to the hope we profess, for he who promised is faithful."

Our hope of salvation and eternal life:

- is "an anchor for the soul,"
- is "firm and secure,"
- inspires "endurance," and
- is "held unswervingly."

How can hope be so certain and firm? It's not because of our ability to think positively. It's because of the One in whom we hope. Our hope isn't in some concept or even a promise. Our hope is in a Person—God Himself. He is trustworthy, dependable, sure, and everlasting. (Read 1 Timothy 6:17 and 1 Peter 1:21 in the margin.)

You may say, "I realize this is true, but my hope is not that strong." Is it possible to be relatively strong in faith and love, yet weak in hope?

Paul had already thanked God for the faith these Christians had in Christ and for their love for one anther (Eph. 1:15). However, in this part of his prayer, he asked that they might know the hope to which God had called them. This indicates they had some uncertainty regarding their eternal destiny. They had strong faith and deep love, but they still needed a strong hope.

"How can this be?" you might ask. Christians who have been taught that their salvation is secure in Christ may have difficulty identifying with these believers. But those of us reared in an environment where salvation is related to good works can easily identify with them.

➤11. **Read the following testimony of how Gene came to experience a secure hope in his salvation.**

**1 Timothy 6:17**

"Command those who are rich in this present world not to be arrogant nor to put their hope in wealth, which is so uncertain, but to put their hope in God, who richly provides us with everything for our enjoyment."

**1 Peter 1:21**

"Through him you believe in God, who raised him from the dead and glorified him, and so your faith and hope are in God."

## FROM DOUBT TO HOPE

I (Gene) can identify with the Ephesian Christians who didn't have a firm hope in their salvation. I was reared in a religious community that had its roots in Switzerland and was started by Samuel Froehlich. Though brought up in a Christian home, he became a rationalist while studying at the University of Basel. Through the study of Scripture, however, he eventually put his faith in Jesus Christ. From the historical record, there's no question that this man truly became a Christian in October 1825.

In 1827, Froehlich was ordained to the ministry in the Protestant state church. However, when he discovered that this church was influenced by the same rationalism that had led him astray, he took a stand against what he felt were abuses in the church. Consequently, he was excommunicated, and eventually he started a new group. As members of this group migrated to America, they eventually formed a denomination called the Apostolic Christian Church.

Though Froehlich became a true believer and eventually reacted to the rationalism in the Protestant state church, the theology he developed included "works" in his formula for salvation. Over the years, the system became even more and more works-oriented.

I was greatly influenced by this theology that mixed faith and works for salvation. I often felt as if I were on a spiritual and emotional roller coaster, never certain that my final descent would ever level out and come to a safe stop. If I felt good emotionally, I then believed that everything was all right between myself and God. If I felt emotionally down, I became very uncertain of my standing before Him. If I failed God in some way—lost my temper, was tempted with some evil thoughts, became too frivolous, wasn't concerned about others as I should be, didn't feel like praying or reading the Bible (all normal feelings and thoughts)—then I seriously questioned my eternal relationship with God. Obviously, my spiritual life was chaotic.

Little by little, through personal study of the Bible, attending youth conferences outside my religious community, and listening to a Christian radio station, I developed a desire to attend a Christian school to learn more about the Scriptures. And so I did, enrolling in Moody Bible Institute in Chicago, which eventually led to my excommunication from this religious group.

Outside of accepting Jesus Christ as my personal Savior, this decision turned out to be the most significant one of my life. At Moody, I discovered that my salvation was secure in Christ—that I had hope—and that I could know for sure, every moment of every day, that my eternal inheritance was guaranteed.

That assurance did not come about without a desperate struggle. For years I had been taught that I couldn't know for sure that I had eternal life until I awakened in eternity and heard God's final words of acceptance or rejection. Even when the truth of Scripture came ringing through loud and clear, the traditions I had been taught often blocked out the reality of these great scriptural statements and filled my heart with doubts. But eventually the "eyes of my heart" were enlightened by the Holy Spirit and I began to understand the hope to which God has called me.

Don't misunderstand. I was a Christian even though I didn't accept my eternal position in Christ. I believed in God and His Son, Jesus Christ. I had faith that Jesus died for me. And I loved my brothers and sisters in Christ. In fact, the church I grew up in was a very caring community—particularly among themselves. However, I constantly wavered in my hope. It depended upon the circumstances of the moment.

I tell this story to illustrate that it's possible to have faith in Christ and love for others—but to have little hope, even as a true believer. This is still true among many believers today, and it was no doubt true of a large segment of the Ephesian Christians. Thus, Paul prayed that they might "know the hope" to which God had called them (Eph. 1:18).

---

**Ephesians 1:17-19**

"I keep asking that the God of our Lord Jesus Christ, the glorious Father, may give you the Spirit of wisdom and revelation, so that you may know him better. I pray also that the eyes of your heart may be enlightened in order that you may know the hope to which he has called you, the riches of his glorious inheritance in the saints, and his incomparably great power for us who believe."

 Pause to reflect on your own sense of hope or doubt about your eternal salvation. Have traditions or teaching from your past caused you to base your salvation on your good works or your faith plus God's grace? We're going to study more about God's grace in Lesson 8. For now, pray that the Holy Spirit will enlighten "the eyes of your heart" so that you may experience the hope of your calling in Christ. Ask God to give you hope in Him. Ask Him to help you understand and believe the truth of Ephesians 2:8-9 below:

"It is by grace you have been saved, through faith—
and this not from yourselves, it is the gift of God—
not by works, so that no one can boast."

 Pray Paul's prayer in Ephesians 1:17-19 (in the margin) for your minichurch members. Name the members one by one, and ask God to help each one come to *experience* the hope of his or her calling in Christ.

## PART 3: RESPONDING TO THE GOD OF HOPE

Some of you who study this lesson will be struggling with the idea that you can have a confident hope in your salvation and eternal life. You may belong to a Christian tradition that teaches you can't have that assurance. Or you still may have difficulty believing God would save a person like you. Don't let this keep you from continuing to seek the Lord. Just as Paul prayed, we pray "that the eyes of your heart may be enlightened in order that you may know the hope to which he has called you" (Eph. 1:18).

Your hope doesn't come from within you. It comes from God. Paul wrote in another letter, "May the <u>God of hope</u> fill you with all joy and peace as you trust in him, so that <u>you may overflow with hope by the power of the Holy Spirit</u>" (Rom. 15:13). Continue to turn your heart and mind toward the God of hope. He will bring you "joy and peace as you trust in him."

➤ **12. Other scriptures tell us more about the hope God develops in us. Read through the following passages, and match each with a statement about hope in the margin. Write a letter beside each verse.**

### GOD'S HOPE IN YOU

A. Suffering produces perseverance, character, and hope.

B. Faith and love spring from hope.

C. Hope inspires endurance.

D. The Body of Christ can help you hold on to hope.

E. Hope encourages purity.

F. Hope will cause others to want to know about Christ.

_____ 1. 1 Peter 3:15—"But in your hearts set apart Christ as Lord. Always be prepared to give an answer to everyone who asks you to give the reason for the <u>hope</u> that you have. But do this with gentleness and respect."

_____ 2. Colossians 1:5—"The faith and love that spring from the <u>hope</u> that is stored up for you in heaven and that you have already heard about in the word of truth, the gospel."

_____ 3. Hebrews 10:23-25—"Let us hold unswervingly to the <u>hope</u> we profess, for he who promised is faithful. And let us consider how we may spur one another on toward love and good deeds. Let us not give up meeting together, as some are in the habit of doing, but let us encourage one another—and all the more as you see the Day approaching."

_____ 4. Romans 5:3-5—"Not only so, but we also rejoice in our sufferings, because we know that suffering produces perseverance; perseverance, character; and character, <u>hope</u>. And <u>hope</u> does not disappoint us, because God has poured out his love into our hearts by the Holy Spirit, whom he has given us."

_____ 5. 1 John 3:2-3—"Dear friends, now we are children of God, and what we will be has not yet been made known. But we know that when he appears, we shall be like him, for we shall see him as he is. Everyone who has this <u>hope</u> in him purifies himself, just as he is pure."

_____ 6. 1 Thessalonians 1:3—"We continually remember before our God and Father your work produced by faith, your labor prompted by love, and your endurance inspired by <u>hope</u> in our Lord Jesus Christ."

(Answers: 1-F; 2-B; 3-D; 4-A; 5-E; 6-C)

When you place your faith in Christ, God begins helping you experience the hope of your calling. He wants you to have joy and peace. Though it may not make sense to you, God may use suffering to develop perseverance, character, and hope in your life. This hope will strengthen your faith, love for others, and spiritual endurance. The Body of Christ (including your minichurch) also can help you move on toward love and good deeds. We can encourage one another. Further, hope leads people to want to be pure as Christ is pure. They will flee from sin because of their love for Christ and the hope He gives. When you have this kind of hope, love, faith, joy, and peace in your life, people will ask you about it. Then you should be prepared to explain the hope you have in Christ.

**13. Based on these truths about hope, how do you think God wants you to respond to Him? Ask Him in prayer. After a time of prayer, check <u>one or more</u> of the following possible responses, or write your own.**

❏ a. I need to let God renew my thinking so I will have hope.

❏ b. I need to ask my minichurch group to pray with me and help me come to experience the hope of my calling in Christ.

❏ c. I need to purify my life and lifestyle so I'll be pure like Christ.

❏ d. I need to prepare to tell others the reason for my hope.

❏ e. I need to become more regular in my meeting with other believers.

❏ f. I need to ask the Lord for help in developing a strong faith and and active love for others.

❏ g. Other: _____

Hope means you can rest in God's love and grace. You can be sure of your salvation. Your emotional ups and downs and your spiritual failures don't change your eternal destiny. This hope does not give you permission to sin, however. These great truths, rightly understood, will draw you closer to God and motivate you to "live lives worthy of God, who calls you into his kingdom and glory" (1 Thess. 2:12).

Experiencing hope in Christ means we have something to share with others who don't have eternal hope. Most people have fixed their hope on things that will eventually fade and pass away. When that happens, they have no hope whatsoever.

### ➤14. Consider the following questions about hope.

• Are you sure of your eternal destiny?  ❏ Yes  ❏ No  If not, you can be sure by accepting Jesus Christ as your personal Savior.

• If you have accepted Jesus Christ as your Savior, do you have moment-by-moment security in Christ?  ❏ Yes  ❏ No  If you don't, you can, for Jesus said He would never leave or forsake you.

• Are you telling others about this hope?  ❏ Yes  ❏ No  If not, you should be, for people everywhere are desperately crying out for hope.

### ➤15. As you read the following experience, begin to think of people you know who need hope.

**Hope, Even in the Face of Death**

My (Gene's) brother Wally serves on our pastoral staff. One day he visited a young man in the hospital who had cancer. The patient, who already had lost his hearing from this dreaded disease, said softly and yet with a sense of finality, "Wally, I'm not going to make it." He immediately began to give instructions to his wife about what he wanted for his funeral. Then he turned to Wally and continued, "Would you say a few words? I don't want a lot of things said; I just want you to be there and say a few words at the funeral."

Knowing Dick could not hear him, Wally took a sheet of paper and wrote, "Dick, thank you for asking me to say a few words. The most important words that I could say are that I am sure you are in heaven with Jesus. You can be sure by asking Jesus into your life. The Bible teaches that this is truth, and the truth will set you free." As Dick read the note, he nodded positively, as if to say, "Yes, that's what I want; that's what I need."

As Wally left the room, the man's wife followed him. She explained with a tearful voice that her husband didn't know what he was saying when he was talking about death.

"Oh, yes he does," Wally responded, calling her by name. You see, my brother had gone through the painful experience of seeing his own wife die from cancer. With compassion and yet directness, he told this young woman that she must come to grips with what her husband was saying. "He's dying!" Wally stated. "And barring a miracle, he won't live."

At that moment, the young woman seemed to understand. From a human point of view, there was no hope. But in Christ there was hope—hope beyond the grave and a hope that even cancer could not take away.

➤16. **Whom do you know who has no hope? Are there some who desperately need hope as they face death or other difficult circumstances? Ask the Lord to bring to your mind people who may need to hear about the hope you have in Christ. The categories in the margin may help you think of some of these people. List their names on the lines below or in the margin.**

wife or husband
children
relatives
neighbors
friends
fellow students
coworkers
business acquaintances
other acquaintances
(barber, clerk, attendant,
salesperson, etc.)

_____

_____

_____

This, then, is one of the most practical applications of what Paul was praying for these Christians and for us. We can offer hope to hurting people. Death is no respecter of persons. At the time of death, all the money in the world offers no hope. All our status, position, talents, and abilities will not provide hope. People all around us are crying out for hope. Sometimes the signal is weak or in a different form. Sometimes it's hidden by anger and defensiveness or behind a wall of silence. Sometimes it's buried deep within and is even covered by a ready smile. But when we understand the signal that people are sending out, we can answer back with assurance, "Yes, there is hope in Jesus Christ!"

"Yes, there is hope
in Jesus Christ!"

➤17. **As you read the following hymn, underline the words and phrases that describe the foundation for your hope. Then thank God for hope! Talk to Him about the response He desires from you today.**

**My Hope Is Built
on Nothing Less**
by Edward Mote

My hope is built on nothing less
Than Jesus' blood and righteousness;
I dare not trust the sweetest frame,
But wholly lean on Jesus' name.

[Refrain]
On Christ, the solid rock, I stand;
All other ground is sinking sand,
All other ground is sinking sand.

## PART 4: EXPERIENCING HIS RICHES AND POWER

Paul used the word *riches* four times in the first three chapters of this letter to describe a believer's blessings in Christ (Eph. 1:18; 2:7; 3:8, 16). How rich is a Christian? Paul carefully outlined these riches. Let's review. In verses 3-14, Paul explained that we have been blessed with all "spiritual blessings in Christ" (Eph. 1:3). To better understand our riches in Christ, Paul described the wonderful reality of life that God has given us in Christ. If you have been born again by placing your faith in Christ, these blessings are yours. These are your spiritual treasures. They have great value.

►18. Review the spiritual blessings listed in the margin. We have personalized them for those who have responded to God's call to salvation. Though each blessing has great value, circle the blessing that is the most precious or that seems to be the most valuable to you. Then on the lines below, briefly describe why that blessing is so meaningful to you.

Why? _____

_____

After describing their spiritual blessings, Paul began to pray for these believers. He prayed that

- God would give them a Spirit of wisdom and revelation
  . . . so they might know God better,
- God would enlighten the eyes of their heart
  . . . so they would know the hope to which He had called them,
  . . . so they would know the riches of His inheritance in the saints,
  . . . so they would know the great power He has for believers.

►19. Which part of Paul's prayer would you most like for God to answer in your own life? Check your response.
  ❑ a. I want to know God better by experiencing Him.
  ❑ b. I want to experience the hope of my salvation.
  ❑ c. I want to know the riches of my inheritance.
  ❑ d. I want to experience God's power working in me.

What Paul outlined in the first part of this letter is the basis of a Christian's hope. If you really understand the riches of your glorious inheritance, you will have hope. You won't waver and be unstable in your Christian life. You won't ride a spiritual roller coaster of feelings about your salvation. All that God has done for you establishes your hope.

A Christian's hope and inheritance are not based on human effort. If they were, we'd surely lose it all! Instead, our position in Christ is based on God's "incomparably great power." This aspect of our salvation and hope is so significant that Paul explained it at length. We're going to study God's power in our next lesson. There's no power greater than God's. We can trust that power not only to provide us with our inheritance in Christ, but also to guarantee that no other force in the universe can take it away from us.

 **Conclude this lesson by reading Romans 8:38-39 in the margin. Thank God for His love and power. Thank Him for all His spiritual blessings. Thank Him for hope. Ask Him to help you grow in your hope and in your ability to share it with others.**

---

**MY SPIRITUAL BLESSINGS**
**Ephesians 1:3-14**

- He chose me.
- He predestined me to be adopted as His child.
- He freely gave me His grace.
- He redeemed me.
- He provided forgiveness for my sins.
- He lavished grace on me, with all wisdom and understanding.
- He made known to me the mystery of His will.
- He included me in Christ.
- He marked me in Christ with the Holy Spirit.
- He guaranteed my inheritance.

♦ **riches:** wealth, abundance, richness, valuable bestowment.

♦ **inheritance:** possessions given to heirs, eternal blessedness.

♦ **power:** force, miraculous power, might, strength, ability.

**Romans 8:38-39**

"For I am convinced that neither death nor life, neither angels nor demons, neither the present nor the future, nor any powers, neither height nor depth, nor anything else in all creation, will be able to separate us from the love of God that is in Christ Jesus our Lord."

# MINICHURCH MEETING 6

## BEFORE THE MEETING

❑ 1. Turn to "Preparing for Your Minichurch Meeting" on page 143. Use it as a guide to get ready for this meeting. Check the box above after you have prepared.

❑ 2. Unless God should direct otherwise, your minichurch leader will be using the following outline to guide your meeting. You may want to look over the questions and activities so you will be better prepared to participate.

## DURING THE MEETING

### ❖ Opening Prayer

### ❖ Singing Together

Consider singing "My Hope Is Built on Nothing Less," "How Firm a Foundation," or "Blessed Assurance" together with other choruses and hymns.

### ❖ Building Relationships

1. Now that we're halfway through our study, let's reflect on what God has done. What one thing has God done or said to you that has been most meaningful or helpful?

2. What aspect of the minichurch meeting has been the most meaningful to you? What do you sense God has done to help you experience what He intended for the Body of Christ to be to one another?

3. What do you sense we could do better or differently to get the most out of our meetings together?

### ❖ Responding to God in Prayer

Thank God for the specific ways He has spoken to you and your minichurch. Thank Him for what He has done in building the relationships between you. Ask Him to help you continue to grow into a healthy and fully mature Body of Christ.

### ❖ Interacting with the Scriptures (in fours or sixes)

1. What verse or passage of Scripture has been most meaningful or challenging to you this week? How has God used it to speak to you? What significant actions have you taken this week because of something God revealed through His Word?

2. (p. 66) Volunteers: Recite the memory verse you learned this week, and explain any special meaning you gained from it.

3. (p. 66, #5) What word or phrase from Ephesians 1:18-19 have you come to better understand or experience this week? Describe your understanding or experience.

### ❖ Reviewing the Lesson

1. What was Paul praying for when he prayed "that the eyes of your heart may be enlightened"?

2. (pp. 67-70) What does the Bible mean by the word *hope*? (#9) What does a Christian hope for? Which of the scriptures about hope was most instructive or meaningful?

3. (p. 70) Where does hope come from—trusting in man and his abilities, or trusting in God?

### ❖ Applying the Truths to Life

1. (p. 67, #6) If you had to summarize your hope of salvation, would it be more like the roller coaster (p. 67) or the anchor (p. 68)? Why?

2. (p. 70, #12) Read each of these verses of Scripture aloud, and discuss your answers.

3. (p. 71, #13 and #14) Based on the truths about hope, how does God want you to respond to Him?

4. (p. 72, #15) What people do you know who need to experience hope? What kind of hope or hopelessness do you see in the people of your community? What do you sense God might want you to do to share hope with them?

5. (p. 73, #18) Which spiritual blessing seems most precious or valuable to you at this time?

6. (p. 73, #19) Which part of Paul's prayer would you most like God to answer in your life? Why?

### ❖ Praying for One Another and for Others
(in fours or sixes)

Based on the things you've just said about hope or the lack of it in your own lives and in the lives of others you know or in your community, spend time praying specifically for each other and for those you've mentioned. Use Paul's prayer that God would enlighten the eyes of your hearts to know hope, riches, and power.

### ❖ Ministering to One Another

What needs (if any) of members have you become aware of during this meeting that the Body needs to care for? What can we do to meet the needs or to help connect the person with those who can help? Are there things we need to do this week to help?

### ❖ Reaching Out to Others

Are there people in your circles of influence who need a saving relationship with Jesus Christ and for whom God seems to be giving you a special burden? What can we pray or do to help you carry that burden?

### ❖ Closing Prayer

### ❖ Optional: "Breaking Bread" Together

# LESSON 7
# EXPERIENCING GOD'S POWER

**The Power of Forgiveness**

While helping a deeply divided church in a series of revival services, I (Claude) had an encounter with "John." John spoke to me on Sunday night. He said he was prepared to do everything in his power to see that this church got straightened out. In his mind, that would require that "those people" leave the church. On Wednesday, I met with the deacons and realized more clearly that John had a spiritual problem. I just couldn't pinpoint what it was.

He, as well as some others, wanted to be in total control of the church. I was especially grieved at his harshness and coldness toward his fellow church members. I prayed more intently because I knew only God could solve the problems this church faced. Only Christ could be in control of the church if it were to become healthy.

The next night, before the service, John pulled me into the pastor's office to talk. John was a large and stern man. He began to sob, and he asked me to forgive him for the way he had spoken to me on Sunday night. Somehow God had brought him under conviction of sin, and he was broken over it. I expressed my forgiveness and asked for permission to pray for him. As I prayed, I mentioned some of what I had seen in his life and asked God to minister to him.

I had seen people like John who felt they always had to be in control. Often I've found that they had a difficult childhood that seemed out of their control. Their only sense of security came when they could totally control their environment. After my prayer, I carefully asked John what life was like for him growing up. He described a stern and harsh father. I asked about his relationship to his dad, and he broke.

"When I was fifteen years old," he began, "our neighbor's barn burned down. Someone told my father she had seen me smoking in the barn and that I was the one who started the fire. I hadn't been there, but my father never stopped to listen to me. He beat me so badly that I had blood running down my back. My mother wouldn't speak to him for three days because of what he had done to me. I've never been able to forgive him. Since then, my dad and I both became Christians. My dad is dead now, but I never was able to forgive him."

I got to guide John through a time of forgiving his dad. We prayed and asked the Lord to heal John of the brokenness, pain, and bitterness he was still carrying around. And God did it! The next night, John asked to tell his story to his church family. He described how God had released him from a heavy burden. The night before, he was able to get a good night's sleep for the first time in months. I saw standing beside me a changed man. I sensed a humility instead of stern pride. I sensed a new tenderness and gentleness instead of harshness. That night, we all saw God's power to change a life right before our eyes. God's resurrection power was what Paul wanted his readers to experience. We want you to know that power experientially as well.

We all saw God's power to change a life right before our eyes.

**Read or Listen to:**

❑ Ephesians 1–6

❑ Ephesians 1–3

❑ Ephesians 1:1-23

**Meaningful Verse or Idea**

_____

_____

_____

**Ephesians 1:19-23**

"That power is like the working of his mighty strength, which he exerted in Christ when he raised him from the dead and seated him at his right hand in the heavenly realms, far above all rule and authority, power and dominion, and every title that can be given, not only in the present age but also in the one to come. And God placed all things under his feet and appointed him to be head over everything for the church, which is his body, the fullness of him who fills everything in every way."

## Part 1: Interacting with the Scripture

### Reading / Hearing God's Word

➤1. Select one of the reading (or listening) options in the margin. Using your Bible, read or listen to the passage of Scripture. As you begin, ask God to speak to you through His Word. Watch for one verse or idea that's especially meaningful to you today. Once you finish reading, check the box indicating the passage you read.

### Meditating on God's Word

➤2. In the margin, write a brief summary of the meaningful verse or idea you just identified.

### Memorizing God's Word

➤3. Select and tear out a new Scripture memory card from the back of your book, or continue reviewing one you started learning earlier. For a new verse, use the tips for memorizing Scripture on your bookmark.

### Understanding God's Word

➤4. Read again the focal passage for this week's lesson (Eph. 1:19-23) in the margin. Underline any key phrases or ideas that seem especially meaningful to you. Then read the brief definitions of key words below. This will prepare you for the remainder of this week's study.

♦ **power:** miraculous force, might, strength, ability.

♦ **rule:** one chief in rank, magistrate, leader.

♦ **authority:** one with delegated influence, jurisdiction, rule of government.

♦ **dominion:** mastery, one who possesses rulership over others.

♦ **head:** supreme, chief, most prominent.

♦ **church:** the whole community of Christians, all saints both in heaven and on earth.

➤5. Look back through this list of words and the words you've underlined in the Scripture passage. Circle one that you would like to understand or experience more fully.

### Looking through the Scripture to God

 **Now take some time to pray to your all-powerful God.**

• Ask Him to help you know and understand the greatness of His power.

• Praise Him for His greatness over all that exists.

• Submit yourself to Christ's headship over you as head of the church.

• Pray Paul's prayer in Ephesians 1:17-19 for yourself and the members of your minichurch, that . . .

– God would give you/them a Spirit of wisdom and revelation

. . . so you/they might know God better,

– God would enlighten the eyes of your/their heart

. . . so you/they would know the hope to which He has called you/them,

. . . so you/they would know the riches of His inheritance in the saints,

. . . so you/they would know the great power He has for believers.

• Close by praying Ephesians 3:16-19 (on your bookmark) for yourself and your minichurch.

## PART 2: PAUL'S KNOWLEDGE OF GOD'S POWER

Paul prayed that the Ephesians would know God's great power for those who believe. This was one of Paul's goals for himself as well.

**Philippians 3:8, 10-11**

"I consider everything a loss compared to the surpassing greatness of knowing Christ Jesus my Lord, for whose sake I have lost all things. I consider them rubbish, that I may gain Christ. . . . I want to know Christ and the power of his resurrection and the fellowship of sharing in his sufferings, becoming like him in his death, and so, somehow, to attain to the resurrection from the dead."

➤6. **Read Philippians 3:8, 10-11 in the margin and answer these questions.**

1. Compared to the greatness of knowing Christ, of what value did Paul count everything else in his life?

_____

2. What did Paul want to know (experientially)? Fill in the blanks.

"I want to know _____ and the _____ of his resurrection and the fellowship of sharing in his _____."

Paul counted everything (even the good things) as "rubbish" and was glad to lose them all if he could just come to an intimate knowledge and experience of Christ. As we studied earlier, this knowledge was not just a mental understanding. Paul wanted to know Jesus' resurrection power by experience. Paul was even willing to know experientially the *sufferings* of Christ so he could become like Him. Do you want to know Jesus that seriously? Paul knew that coming to know Christ intimately would be costly. Yet everything he had to give up was rubbish by comparison.

➤7. **How seriously do you want to know Christ and His resurrection power in your life? Check the response closest to your own.**
   ❑ a. Lord, I'm like Paul. I want to know You and Your power no matter what the cost. I want to be like You.
   ❑ b. Lord, my head says yes but my feelings say no. I'm not sure I'm willing to suffer loss in order to know Jesus that way.
   ❑ c. Lord, I'll settle for just knowing about You with my mind.
   ❑ d. Lord, I'm struggling. Would You help me to come to the place that I would want to know You that seriously? Please help me.

People normally don't like to suffer physically or in any other way. Consequently, you may be struggling with the cost of knowing Christ and His resurrection power. If you weren't ready to check the *a* response above, however, it's probably because you don't know enough about God's "incomparably great power." If you really knew Christ and the power you can experience, you—like Paul—would count everything you have to give up as trash in comparison.

**Matthew 13:44-45**

"'The kingdom of heaven is like treasure hidden in a field. When a man found it, he hid it again, and then in his joy went and sold all he had and bought that field.

"Again, the kingdom of heaven is like a merchant looking for fine pearls. When he found one of great value, he went away and sold everything he had and bought it.'"

Jesus told two parables related to this issue. In one He said a farmer was plowing a field and discovered a buried treasure of great value. He went home immediately, sold everything he had, and bought the field (and the valuable treasure). In the other a pearl merchant found a pearl of great value and sold everything to buy it. (Read Matthew 13:44-45 in the margin.) In both cases the value of the thing purchased was far greater than everything given up. Jesus said, "The kingdom of heaven is like" this.

When Paul prayed that the Ephesians would know God's power, he knew it was of great value. He wrote to the church at Corinth, "My message and my preaching were not with wise and persuasive words, but with a demonstration of the Spirit's power, so that your faith might not rest on men's wisdom, but on God's power" (1 Cor. 2:4-5). God's power at work through Paul's life is what God used to draw the Corinthians to faith in Christ.

Paul also talked about God's power to Timothy—Paul's apprentice in ministry. He described how this power should affect our witness.

**2 Timothy 1:7-9**

"For God did not give us a spirit of timidity, but a spirit of power, of love and of self-discipline.

"So do not be ashamed to testify about our Lord, or ashamed of me his prisoner. But join with me in suffering for the gospel, by the power of God, who has saved us and called us to a holy life—not because of anything we have done but because of his own purpose and grace."

➤ 8. **Read 2 Timothy 1:7-9 in the margin, and answer these questions:**

1. Instead of a spirit of timidity (fear), what kind of spirit has God given us? A spirit of . . .

   _____

2. Timothy evidently was ashamed to do what about the Lord?

   _____

3. What did Paul invite Timothy to join him in?

   _____

Timothy evidently had grown fearful and timid about testifying publicly about the Lord. He saw Paul's sufferings in prison and hesitated to risk himself in the same way. However, God's gift to believers is a "spirit of power, of love and of self-discipline." Therefore, Paul invited Timothy to join in suffering for the gospel—it was worth it all!

Earlier in his own ministry, Paul had learned one of God's great purposes in suffering. God had revealed such great things to Paul that he could have become spiritually proud. But God used suffering for a purpose.

➤ 9. **As you read what God taught Paul below, underline God's answer to Paul when He refused to take away Paul's "thorn." Also, circle the word *power* each time it occurs.**

"To keep me from becoming conceited because of these surpassingly great revelations, there was given me a thorn in my flesh, a messenger of Satan, to torment me. Three times I pleaded with the Lord to take it away from me. But he said to me, 'My grace is sufficient for you, for my power is made perfect in weakness.' Therefore I will boast all the more gladly about my weaknesses, so that Christ's power may rest on me. That is why, for Christ's sake, I delight in weaknesses, in insults, in hardships, in persecutions, in difficulties. For when I am weak, then I am strong" (2 Cor. 12:7-10).

God allowed Paul to suffer and know a personal weakness so that God's power might be perfected in Paul. Paul learned that his personal weaknesses provided the ideal opportunity for God to reveal His strength. When Paul was weak, Christ's power rested on him. Therefore, Paul boasted in his weaknesses. He delighted in his difficulties because he knew that God could be glorified through his life most clearly in those times.

➤ 10. **Based on Paul's example, how should you respond to your own weaknesses? Check the correct response.**

   ❑ a. I should hide my weaknesses so that everyone thinks I'm strong.
   ❑ b. I should welcome difficulties so that God's power may be revealed.
   ❑ c. I should beg and plead with God until He removes the difficulties.

   Talk to the Lord about areas of weakness, hardship, insult, or difficulties you face. Ask Him to work in those areas to reveal His power.

## PART 3: GOD'S POWER REVEALED

One day, some Jewish leaders were trying to trap Jesus with their questions. He responded by saying, "You are in error because you do not know the Scriptures or the power of God" (Matt. 22:29). God has revealed Himself in the Scriptures. This is one of the reasons you need to be reading and studying your Bible. Without it, you could be in great error and not even know it. In the Bible, you'll learn about the many ways God has revealed His mighty power. But you also need to have an experiential knowledge. God didn't quit showing His power at the end of the first century. His power is real and active today, too, and it's available to all believers.

**Examples of God's Power**

1. _____

2. _____

3. _____

4. _____

5. _____

➤11. **Based on your knowledge of Scripture, what are some of the ways God revealed His power in the Bible? Make a list in the margin of up to five things God did.**

God has revealed His power in many ways throughout the Bible.

➤12. **Read the following examples, and circle the word *power* in each one.**
   • **In creation:** "Ah, Sovereign LORD, you have made the heavens and the earth by your great power and outstretched arm. Nothing is too hard for you" (Jer. 32:17).
   • **In delivering Israel from Egypt:** "When the Israelites saw the great power the LORD displayed against the Egyptians, the people feared the LORD and put their trust in him and in Moses his servant" (Ex. 14:31).
   • **In giving Israel the promised land:** "Power and might are in your hand, and no one can withstand you. O our God, did you not drive out the inhabitants of this land before your people Israel and give it forever to the descendants of Abraham your friend?" (2 Chron. 20:6-7).
   • **In giving Jesus to us through the virgin Mary:** "The angel answered, 'The Holy Spirit will come upon you, and the power of the Most High will overshadow you. So the holy one to be born will be called the Son of God. . . . For nothing is impossible with God'" (Luke 1:35, 37).
   • **In the miracles of Jesus:** "All the people were amazed and said to each other, 'What is this teaching? With authority and power he gives orders to evil spirits and they come out!'" (Luke 4:36). "One day as he was teaching . . . the power of the Lord was present for him to heal the sick" (Luke 5:17).

**Ephesians 1:18-19**

"I pray also that the eyes of your heart may be enlightened in order that you may know … his incomparably great power for us who believe. That power is like the working of his mighty strength."

**God's Power**

_____

_____

_____

You could have named many other examples. In his prayer for the saints, Paul described God's power. He wanted to make sure they clearly understood it. In Ephesians 1:18-19, he used four different words to describe this power.
   ◆ **power:** (comes from the Greek word from which we get our English word *dynamite*) the ability to accomplish what is planned, promised, or started.
   ◆ **working:** (comes from the Greek word from which we get our English word *energy*) to produce, perform.
   ◆ **mighty:** power to resist and overcome obstacles or opponents.
   ◆ **strength:** the actual exercise of power.

These four words graphically describe God's unmatched power. He definitely has the ability to carry out what He has planned and promised. His very nature is strength and power. No obstacle or force can withstand His might. "For nothing is impossible with God" (Luke 1:37).

➤13. **In your own words, write a description of God's power in the margin. If you prefer, you could write a brief poem.**

**Resurrection Power.** Paul went on to describe God's power as that "which he exerted in Christ when he raised him from the dead and seated him at his right hand in the heavenly realms" (Eph. 1:20). Paul's major concern was that these Christians understand fully the power that was demonstrated in Christ, first when He was raised from the dead and then when He ascended to once again be with the Father.

Jesus Christ died on the cross, but He didn't remain a dead man. The mighty power of God was released, and He came forth from the tomb on the third day. When we place our faith in Christ for the forgiveness of our sins, we can experience this resurrection power.

• **Romans 6:8**—"If we died with Christ, we believe that we will also live with him."

• **Romans 6:18**—"You have been set free from sin and have become slaves to righteousness."

• **Romans 6:22-23**—"Now that you have been set free from sin and have become slaves to God, the benefit you reap leads to holiness, and the result is eternal life. For the wages of sin is death, but the gift of God is eternal life in Christ Jesus our Lord."

➤14. **Read through the verses from Romans 6 below and in the margin. Underline the words or phrases that describe our new relationship to sin and the life we can have in Christ. We underlined two for you.**

• Romans 6:2-4 —"We <u>died to sin</u>; how can we live in it any longer? Or don't you know that all of us who were baptized into Christ Jesus were baptized into his death? We were therefore buried with him through baptism into death in order that, just as Christ was raised from the dead through the glory of the Father, <u>we too may live a new life</u>."

• Romans 6:6—"Our old self was crucified with him so that the body of sin might be done away with, that we should no longer be slaves to sin."

• Romans 6:11-14—"Count yourselves dead to sin but alive to God in Christ Jesus. Therefore do not let sin reign in your mortal body so that you obey its evil desires. Do not offer the parts of your body to sin, as instruments of wickedness, but rather offer yourselves to God, as those who have been brought from death to life; and offer the parts of your body to him as instruments of righteousness. For sin shall not be your master."

When you experience God's resurrection power, you are raised to a new life. You become a slave to God and to righteousness. Your benefits include holiness. You're dead to sin, set free from sin, no longer a slave to sin, no longer under its mastery.

➤15. **To what degree are you experiencing the fullness of God's resurrection power in your life? Check your response or write your own.**

❑ a. I'm experiencing a deadness to sin. God is giving victory. I haven't arrived perfectly, but I'm living on the victory side!

❑ b. I never knew I had that kind of victory over sin available to me. I've never counted myself dead to sin and alive to God.

❑ c. I'm still losing too many battles with sin. I need to yield myself fully to God and refuse to live in sin any longer.

❑ d. Other: _____

_____

_____

**God's Ruling Power.** This power that raised Christ from the dead also placed Him "far above all rule and authority, power and dominion, and every title that can be given, not only in the present age, but also in the one to come" (Eph. 1:21). Jesus is the ruler of all rulers. He is the supreme power who governs over all other powers in heaven and on earth—even all demonic powers. And "God exalted him to the highest place and gave him the name that is above every name, that at the name of Jesus every knee should bow, in heaven and on earth and under the earth, and every tongue confess that Jesus Christ is Lord, to the glory of God the Father" (Phil. 2:9-11).

Furthermore, "God placed all things under his feet and appointed him to be head over everything for the church, which is his body, the fullness of him who fills everything in every way" (Eph. 1:22). With this statement, Paul seemed to be saying that the church of Jesus Christ was and is God's greatest and most glorious creation and the ultimate in demonstrating His "incomparable" power. When you see, know, and experience God's great power, you can't help but want to praise Him and worship Him.

➤16. **Use these words from Scripture as your own prayers of praise and worship. Spend some time praising God and expressing your worship to Him. You may want to write your own prayer of praise to the Lord in the margin. You may enjoy reading these words aloud:**

**My Prayer of Praise**

_____

_____

_____

_____

_____

_____

_____

_____

_____

_____

_____

_____

**1 Chronicles 29:10-13**—"Praise be to you, O LORD, God of our father Israel, from everlasting to everlasting. Yours, O LORD, is the greatness and the power and the glory and the majesty and the splendor, for everything in heaven and earth is yours. Yours, O LORD, is the kingdom; you are exalted as head over all. Wealth and honor come from you; you are the ruler of all things. In your hands are strength and power to exalt and give strength to all. Now, our God, we give you thanks, and praise your glorious name."

**Psalm 20:6-7**—"Now I know that the LORD saves his anointed; he answers him from his holy heaven with the saving power of his right hand. Some trust in chariots and some in horses, but we trust in the name of the LORD our God."

**Psalm 63:1-3**—"O God, you are my God, earnestly I seek you; my soul thirsts for you, my body longs for you, in a dry and weary land where there is no water. I have seen you in the sanctuary and beheld your power and your glory. Because your love is better than life, my lips will glorify you."

**Psalm 66:1-5**—"Shout with joy to God, all the earth! Sing the glory of his name; make his praise glorious! Say to God, 'How awesome are your deeds! So great is your power that your enemies cringe before you. All the earth bows down to you; they sing praise to you, they sing praise to your name.' _Selah_. Come and see what God has done, how awesome his works in man's behalf!"

**Psalm 68:34-35**—"Proclaim the power of God, whose majesty is over Israel, whose power is in the skies. You are awesome, O God, in your sanctuary; the God of Israel gives power and strength to his people. Praise be to God!"

## Part 4: Responding to God

You already have begun responding to God through praise and worship. That's a natural response when you experience His power, or even when you hear about it. If you're a Christian, you already have experienced God's power at work in and around your life.

➤17. **What are some of the ways you already have experienced God's power? Check any of these ways you've experienced it.**

❑ forgiveness of sin                    ❑ answered prayer
❑ deliverance from a difficulty         ❑ protection from harm
❑ physical healing                      ❑ emotional healing
❑ victory over a sinful habit           ❑ strength in the face of problems
❑ endurance in time of suffering        ❑ patience in a time of conflict
❑ self-control in temptation            ❑ reconciled relationships
❑ being gifted and used by God to see another life changed
❑ power and boldness in my witness

➤18. **Take a few minutes to think of specific times when you remember experiencing God's power at work in or through your life. Write some notes to yourself in the margin.**

Your knowledge and experience of God's power should affect you in a number of ways. They should cause you to be secure in Christ because of hope. This is what Paul was praying about in Ephesians 1:18. This also is what the apostle Peter had in mind when he wrote his first letter.

➤19. **Read 1 Peter 1:3-5 in the margin, and circle the key words that describe the security of your inheritance.**

God's power is shielding and protecting your eternal inheritance! It will "never perish, spoil or fade." A true knowledge of God's power should also develop in you a spirit of humility. This doesn't mean weakness, however! God has shared some of His power with mankind, but all we can ever accomplish is minute compared with God's accomplishments. All that we are and have and all we can do is because of His power—not ours!

➤20. **What is at least one way an experience of God's power should affect you?**

_____

A knowledge of God's power should be reassuring in the midst of pressure and problems. David Livingstone, a famous missionary and explorer, was surrounded by hostile, angry natives in the heart of Africa. He was in danger of losing his life and contemplated fleeing in the night. But in the night, something happened. He recorded it in his diary on January 14, 1856:

> "I felt much turmoil of spirit in prospect of having all my plans for the welfare of this great region and this teeming population knocked on the head by savages tomorrow. But I read that Jesus said: 'All power is given unto Me in heaven and in earth. Go ye therefore and teach all nations, and lo, I am with you always, even unto the end of the world.' It is the word of a gentleman of the most strict and sacred honor, so there is an end to it! . . . Should such a man as I flee? Nay, verily, . . . I feel quite calm now, thank God!"

---

**Notes**

_____

_____

_____

_____

_____

_____

_____

**1 Peter 1:3-5**

"Praise be to the God and Father of our Lord Jesus Christ! In his great mercy he has given us new birth into a living hope through the resurrection of Jesus Christ from the dead, and into an inheritance that can never perish, spoil or fade— kept in heaven for you, who through faith are shielded by God's power until the coming of the salvation that is ready to be revealed in the last time."

**Some Ways Knowledge and Experience of God's Power Affect Me**

1. Make me secure in Christ.
2. Make me humble instead of arrogant or proud.
3. Give me assurance in the midst of pressure and problems.

**Philippians 4:5-7**

"The Lord is near. Do not be anxious about anything, but in everything, by prayer and petition, with thanksgiving, present your requests to God. And the peace of God, which transcends all understanding, will guard your hearts and your minds in Christ Jesus."

**Exodus 9:16**

"I have raised you up for this very purpose, that I might show you my power and that my name might be proclaimed in all the earth."

**Acts 1:8**

"You will receive power when the Holy Spirit comes on you; and you will be my witnesses... to the ends of the earth."

**Psalm 71:17-18**

"Since my youth, O God, you have taught me, and to this day I declare your marvelous deeds. Even when I am old and gray, do not forsake me, O God, till I declare your power to the next generation, your might to all who are to come."

**Psalm 77:11-15**

"I will remember the deeds of the LORD; yes, I will remember your miracles of long ago. I will meditate on all your works and consider all your mighty deeds. Your ways, O God, are holy. What god is so great as our God? You are the God who performs miracles; you display your power among the peoples. With your mighty arm you redeemed your people."

Like Paul, David Livingstone understood the power of God. Whether by life or by death, he was willing to face the unknown. No matter what happened, he knew he would be delivered. He would either live to continue with his ministry or be taken home to heaven and set totally free. God gave Livingstone another 17 years of ministry after that night. When he finally died, he was found by his native friends in a peaceful state, kneeling in the posture of prayer. His body was returned to England for a hero's burial in Westminster Abbey. Because of God's power, he came to know the peace of God that passes understanding (Phil. 4:5-7).

▶**21. Read Philippians 4:5-7 in the margin. Do you know that kind of peace?**

❑ Yes.  ❑ No, not right now.  ❑ No, I never have.

Because God is near to His children, you can know a peace that's beyond understanding. If you don't already know that peace, you may want to pause and talk to the Lord about it. According to the Scriptures, God reveals His power and gives us power for a variety of other reasons. Some of those are listed below.

- that His name might be proclaimed throughout the earth (Ex. 9:16)
- that people would fear and reverence Him and put their trust in Him (Ex. 14:31)
- that people would worship Him only and follow His commands and decrees (2 Kings 17:36-39)
- to avoid error and the practice of unbelief (Matt. 22:29)
- to provide power to witness (Acts 1:8)
- to draw people to faith in Christ (1 Cor. 2:4-5)
- to discipline the sinful in the church (1 Cor. 5:4-5)
- to make us strong in spiritual warfare (Eph. 6:10-18)
- to make us like Christ in eternity (Phil. 3:21)

God wants us to respond to the knowledge and experience of His power. An example of one of those responses is found in Psalm 71.

▶**22. Read the prayer in Psalm 71:17-18 in the margin. Underline what the psalmist wanted to do before he died.**

The psalmist wanted to live long enough to tell the next generation all about the power of the Lord. That's one of the ways you can respond to your experience of God's power.

▶**23. What is a way you would be willing to tell of God's power to the next generation? Check one or more ways below. If you have another idea, write your own.**

❑ Read or tell Bible stories to my children and grandchildren.
❑ Teach a children's Bible class.
❑ Recall with my family the ways God has blessed me and us.
❑ Share a testimony with others about God's work in my life.
❑ Keep a journal (written, audio, or video) of my experiences of God's presence and power, and give copies to my children.
❑ Other: _____

 **As you conclude this lesson, pray through Psalm 77:11-15 in the margin. Take time to praise and thank God for the ways you have experienced His power. Meditate on all He has done for you. Ask Him to give you opportunities to tell others of His power. Pray that the members of your minichurch would know His power.**

# MINICHURCH MEETING 7

## BEFORE THE MEETING

❑ 1. Turn to "Preparing for Your Minichurch Meeting" on page 143. Use it as a guide to get ready for this meeting. Check the box above after you have prepared.

❑ 2. Unless God should direct otherwise, your minichurch leader will be using the following outline to guide your meeting. You may want to look over the questions and activities so you will be better prepared to participate.

## DURING THE MEETING

### ❖ Opening Prayer

### ❖ Singing Together

Consider singing "How Great Thou Art" or "All Hail the Power of Jesus' Name" together with other choruses and hymns.

### ❖ Building Relationships

1. (p. 82, #17 and #18) What's one of the most memorable or special ways you have experienced God's power at work in or around your life?

2. (in fours or sixes) In what area of your spiritual life do you sense a need to experience God's power? How can we pray for you?

### ❖ Praying for One Another (in fours or sixes)

After all have stated ways they sense a need to experience God's power, pray for one another. Ask the Lord to administer His power in the lives of your brothers and sisters in Christ in ways that will meet their needs and bring Him glory. Be specific. Make sure you pray for each person by name.

### ❖ Interacting with the Scriptures (in fours or sixes)

1. What verse or passage of Scripture has been most meaningful or challenging to you this week? How has God used it to speak to you? What significant actions have you taken this week because of something God revealed through His Word?

2. (p. 76) Volunteers: Recite the memory verse you learned this week, and explain any special meaning you gained from it.

3. (p. 76, #5) What word or phrase from Ephesians 1:19-23 have you come to better understand or experience this week? Describe your understanding or experience.

### ❖ Reviewing the Lesson

1. How did Paul experience God's power?

2. (p. 79, #11) How has God revealed His power in the Bible?

3. (p. 79) What four words did Paul use to describe God's

power, and what do we learn from each? (#13) How did you describe God's power?

4. (p. 83) What reasons are given in Scripture for why God reveals His power or gives us His power? Which of these have you experienced?

### ❖ Applying the Truths to Life

1. (p. 80) How would you describe God's resurrection power? What difference does that power make in a believer's life with regard to his struggle with temptation and sin?

2. (p. 77, #7) How seriously do you want to know God's resurrection power? What difference do you think it might make in your life?

3. (p. 78, #10) How should you respond to your weaknesses? Why? How do you normally respond to your weaknesses?

4. (p. 80, #15) To what degree are you experiencing the fullness of God's power in relation to sin? Think of one person you know who seems to be living in this kind of victory over sin. What's the evidence of his or her victory?

5. (p. 82) Discuss the three ways (in the margin) a knowledge and experience of God's power should affect you. Which of these is more true of your life?

6. (p. 83, #23) What are some ways you can tell the next generation about God's power? What, if anything, do you sense God wants you to do?

### ❖ Responding to God in Prayer

1. (p. 81) If you wrote one, read your prayer of praise from the margin. Take turns reading some of the Bible's prayers of praise on this page.

2. Consider singing a hymn or chorus of praise to the Lord—one that's a prayer expressing praise and worship to the Lord. Then pray sentence prayers of praise to the Lord for the evidences of His power.

### ❖ Ministering to One Another / Reaching Out

Discuss the possibility of preparing a video journal with testimonies of God's power to change lives. The journal could recount for the next generation what God has done in your church. You could focus on specific topics like God's power to change marriages, to bring victory over alcohol (or drugs), or to save a wayward child (or lost spouse). Clips from the video could be used in worship services, or tapes on a topic could be played for people facing a particular problem. The testimonies could be used by God to increase faith and point others to Himself. If God should call you to a project like this, you'll probably want to involve others in your church.

### ❖ Closing Prayer

### ❖ Optional: "Breaking Bread" Together

# Lesson 8
# Experiencing God's Grace

**A Policeman's "Grace"**

One day following an appointment, I (Gene) was driving back to my office when I suddenly noticed a police car behind me. I immediately looked at my speedometer and breathed a sigh of relief when I saw I wasn't speeding. A few blocks later, the policeman pulled his car up beside me. We traveled together, side by side, for about a mile. Periodically I glanced at him, and I could see he was looking back at me. But I knew I wasn't breaking the law, so I was pretty relaxed—in fact, a bit proud of myself for having maintained the speed limit.

Finally, I pulled up to an expressway. After making the turn, I decided to stay on the service road, while the policeman pulled out onto the highway. Again we traveled side by side—he on the expressway and me on the service road. And again we periodically glanced at each other. To my surprise, the policeman pulled off the main road at the next exit, came in behind me, and turned on his flashing lights. I saw them immediately and pulled to an abrupt stop. He got out of his car, walked up to my window, and cordially introduced himself. He asked for my driver's license, checked it out, and then made some observations that left me speechless.

"Sir," he said, "back on the road before we turned onto the main highway, you failed to make a complete stop at. . . . That's violation number one. When you reached the expressway, you failed to observe the yield sign. That's violation number two. When we were traveling side by side, you on the service road and me on the highway, you were over the speed limit on the service road. That's violation number three. And finally," he said, pointing to my windshield, "your inspection sticker is overdue! That's violation number four."

At that point, I wished I had an ejection seat or some "invisibility pills" to be able to escape that man's presence. My embarrassment was overwhelming. I could see tomorrow's newspaper headline: "Pastor guilty of four violations in full view of police officer."

"However," he continued, "I have a fugitive with me. I have to get him to the station immediately and don't have time to write out a ticket. But I wanted to warn you. Good day," he said with a smile. "And do be careful!" He then got in his car and went on his way. I sat there for a few moments, trying to recap what I had been thinking. In full view of that officer, I had consistently violated the law, but I was totally unaware of my unlawful acts. In fact, I had felt secure in what I thought was righteous behavior.

Once I cleared my head and again began to breathe normally, I came to one basic conclusion: "Gene Getz, that's an illustration of pure grace. That man could have 'thrown the book at you.'" I'm not proud of this incident. I relate it because it illustrates, in a human way, what grace is about. The apostle Paul, in the next section of his letter to the Ephesians, focused on the subject of grace—God's grace toward us.

**Read or Listen to:**

❑ Ephesians 1–6

❑ Ephesians 1–3

❑ Ephesians 2:1-22

**Meaningful Verse or Idea**

_____

_____

_____

♦ **transgressions:** breaking the law, willfully crossing the line.

♦ **sins:** missing of the mark, errors, wrongdoing.

♦ **wrath:** thoughtful anger, indignation, judgment, vengeance.

♦ **love:** [_agape_] godly affection, seeking the best for another unconditionally.

♦ **mercy:** pity, active compassion that meets needs.

♦ **grace:** undeserved favor, free gift.

♦ **saved:** given eternal salvation, delivered, made whole.

♦ **kindness:** gentleness, goodness, excellence in character or demeanor.

♦ **faith:** reliance upon Christ for salvation, trust.

♦ **gift:** a present, something given freely.

♦ **works:** acts, deeds, activities, actions.

♦ **boast:** claim credit, take glory for self.

♦ **workmanship:** a product, that which is made.

## Part 1: Interacting with the Scriptures

### Reading / Hearing God's Word

➤1. Select one of the reading (or listening) options in the margin. Using your Bible, read or listen to the passage of Scripture. As you begin, ask God to speak to you through His Word. Watch for one verse or idea that's especially meaningful to you. Once you finish reading, check the box indicating the passage you read.

### Meditating on God's Word

➤2. In the margin, write a brief summary of the meaningful verse or idea you just identified.

### Memorizing God's Word

➤3. Select and tear out a new Scripture memory card from the back of your book, or continue reviewing one you started learning earlier. For a new verse, use the tips for memorizing Scripture on your bookmark.

### Understanding God's Word

➤4. Read below the focal passage for this week's lesson (Eph. 2:1-10). Underline any key phrases or ideas that seem especially meaningful to you. Then read the brief definitions of key words in the margin. This will prepare you for the remainder of this week's study.

> **Ephesians 2:1-10**—"As for you, you were dead in your transgressions and sins, in which you used to live when you followed the ways of this world and of the ruler of the kingdom of the air, the spirit who is now at work in those who are disobedient. All of us also lived among them at one time, gratifying the cravings of our sinful nature and following its desires and thoughts. Like the rest, we were by nature objects of wrath. But because of his great love for us, God, who is rich in mercy, made us alive with Christ even when we were dead in transgressions—it is by grace you have been saved. And God raised us up with Christ and seated us with him in the heavenly realms in Christ Jesus, in order that in the coming ages he might show the incomparable riches of his grace, expressed in his kindness to us in Christ Jesus. For it is by grace you have been saved, through faith—and this not from yourselves, it is the gift of God—not by works, so that no one can boast. For we are God's workmanship, created in Christ Jesus to do good works, which God prepared in advance for us to do."

➤5. Look through the list of key words in the margin. Circle one that you would like to understand or experience more fully.

### Looking through the Scripture to God

 Now pause to pray.

- Ask the Lord to help you understand the difference between being dead apart from Christ and alive in Christ.
- Ask the Lord to help you understand and experience more of His love, mercy, kindness, and grace.
- Thank the Lord for the free gift of salvation.
- Ask the Lord to give you a love for others who are "dead" in sin.
- Close by praying Ephesians 1:17-19 and 3:16-19 (on your bookmark) for yourself and your minichurch.

## PART 2: UNDESERVED GRACE

In our text for this lesson, Paul described the desperate condition of those who have not experienced salvation by God's grace. Because of His love for us, God has offered His grace to all who are spiritually dead in their sins. This grace is God's undeserved favor toward us. When we place our faith in Christ, God brings us from death to spiritual life.

♦ **grace:** undeserved favor, free gift.

➤6. **This text gives us a description of a person <u>before</u> salvation and <u>after</u> salvation. Mark the following statements "B" if they describe the "before" condition and "A" if they describe the condition after salvation.**

_____ 1. alive with Christ

_____ 2. dead in transgressions and sins

_____ 3. follows the ways and standards of the world

_____ 4. follows the ways of Satan and is disobedient

_____ 5. gives in to the desires and thoughts of the sinful nature

_____ 6. made new in Christ to do good works

_____ 7. objects deserving God's wrath

_____ 8. raised up and seated with Christ in heaven

_____ 9. recipients of His kindness

_____ 10. saved from the penalty of sin

God's grace takes us from death to life, from sin to good works, from deserving God's wrath to being received in heaven. What a change God brings about when He saves us. (Answers: B=2, 3, 4, 5, 7; A=1, 6, 8, 9, 10)

➤7. **Read or sing (if you know the tune) the following hymn. Meditate on the greatness of God's grace, which washes away our sin and guilt.**

**Grace Greater Than Our Sin**
by Julia H. Johnston

Marvelous grace of our loving Lord,
Grace that exceeds our sin and our guilt,
Yonder on Calvary's mount outpoured,
There where the blood of the Lamb was spilt.

[Refrain]
Grace, grace, God's grace, grace that will pardon and cleanse within;
Grace, grace, God's grace, grace that is greater than all our sin.

Dark is the stain that we cannot hide,
What can avail to wash it away?
Look! There is flowing a crimson tide;
Whiter than snow you may be today.

Marvelous, infinite, matchless grace,
Freely bestowed on all who believe;
You that are longing to see His face,
Will you this moment His grace receive?

When Paul said, "As for you, you were dead in your transgressions and sins" (Eph. 2:1), he was referring to the Gentile believers who had been "included in Christ" when they had heard "the word of truth" (Eph. 1:13). In verse 3 he included all believers, both Jews and Gentiles. Thus we read, "All of us also lived among them [in the ways of the world] at one time, gratifying the cravings of our sinful nature and following its desires and thoughts. Like the rest, we [unsaved Jews] were by nature objects of wrath" (Eph. 2:3). God's grace is needed by both Jews and Gentiles. Because of sin and rebellion against God's rule, every human being ("all of us") deserves God's wrath. Everyone needs God's grace.

♦ **love:** [*agape*] godly affection, seeking the best for another unconditionally.

**Because of His Love.** In verses 4-7, Paul gave at least three reasons why God has made His grace available to all humanity. The first is God's great love. Jesus Himself said, "For God so loved the world that he gave his one and only Son, that whoever believes in him shall not perish but have eternal life" (John 3:16). God created us for a love relationship with Himself. His desire is for us to spend eternity with Him. Because of love, He provided grace.

➤8. What's one reason God offered His grace to us?

Because of His _____

♦ **mercy:** pity, active compassion that meets needs.

**Because of His Mercy.** God has taken pity on sinful humanity. He knew we couldn't save ourselves. Because of sin, we never could achieve a right standing in our own abilities or strength. But God is merciful. That's His nature. He is "rich in mercy," so He met our deepest need by providing a remedy for our sin problem.

➤9. In addition to love, what's another reason God has provided grace?

Because of His _____

♦ **kindness:** gentleness, goodness, excellence in character or demeanor.

**Because of His Kindness.** There's an interesting correlation between the raising of Lazarus and what God has done for us. In Ephesians 2:6-7, we read that "God raised us up with Christ and seated us with him in the heavenly realms in Christ Jesus, in order that in the coming ages he might show the incomparable riches of his grace, expressed in his kindness to us in Christ Jesus." God's mercy toward us focuses on His compassion. God's "kindness" toward us focuses on His love in action.

Jesus dramatically illustrated this quality of kindness when He told the story of the Good Samaritan. A man was traveling from Jerusalem to Jericho and was attacked by robbers. They tore off his clothes, beat him, and left him half dead. A priest was traveling on the road but passed by on the other side. Next a Levite came by and when he saw him he also moved over to the other side of the road. But then a Samaritan approached the scene of this tragic event. Jesus said, "When he saw him, he took pity on him" (Luke 10:33). That's mercy!

We go on to read that the Samaritan "went to him and bandaged his wounds, pouring on oil and wine. Then he put the man on his own donkey, took him to an inn and took care of him" (Luke 10:34). And the next morning when he left the inn, he gave the proprietor some money. "Look after him," he said, "and when I return, I will reimburse you for any extra expense you may have" (Luke 10:35). That's kindness!

In a beautiful way, the story of the Good Samaritan illustrates all the reasons God made His grace available to mankind. The source of His divine grace is His love, which has been demonstrated by His compassionate mercy and unselfish kindness.

➤10. **Match the reason God gives us His grace on the left with the correct definition on the right. Write the number beside the letter.**

    1. Love            ____ a. Gentleness, goodness

    2. Mercy          ____ b. Seeking the best for another unconditionally

    3. Kindness     ____ c. Pity and active compassion that meets needs

Anyone who has experienced salvation in Jesus Christ is a recipient of God's unearned favor—His grace. No one deserves salvation because of his or her good life. No one can do enough good works. When Jews are saved, they're saved by God's grace. When Gentiles are saved, they also are saved by God's grace. Every category of human being who has ever been saved was saved by God's grace. (Answers: 1-b; 2-c; 3-a)

Turn to the Lord to express your gratitude for His grace. Agree with Him that you're not worthy of His grace. Then thank Him for His love, mercy, and kindness shown to you through salvation.

## PART 3: SALVATION IS A GIFT

Some people have been taught that salvation is available only to those who do the right things. Perhaps you've heard some of the reasons listed below as evidence that a person deserves to go to heaven.

➤11. **Check all the following reasons you've heard given for salvation or for going to heaven:**
- ❑ attending church regularly
- ❑ being a faithful member of the church or the lodge
- ❑ being born into a family that belongs to the church
- ❑ dying in a "holy war" supported by the church
- ❑ following the rules of my leader or the church
- ❑ giving large amounts of money to God's work
- ❑ keeping the Ten Commandments and being a good person
- ❑ receiving baptism, the Lord's Supper, and other religious rites
- ❑ taking a trip or performing an act that requires great sacrifice
- ❑ taking care of the poor and needy
- ❑ serving as a missionary or pastor
- ❑ showing my love for God by a great physical sacrifice or suffering

Though many of these things are good, none measure up to the requirements for salvation. It's a gift that cannot be earned by good works. Paul said, "It is by grace you have been saved, through faith—and this not from yourselves, it is the gift of God— not by works, so that no one can boast" (Eph. 2:8-9).

➤12. **Review the definitions of key words in the margin. Then read again Ephesians 2:8-9 above, and circle the key words in the text.**

➤13. **Through which of the following does salvation come? Check one.**
- ❑ a. Through faith in Christ.
- ❑ b. Through good works.

➤14. **Who is the only source of your salvation? Check one.**
- ❑ a. God is the source of my salvation. It's a gift from Him.
- ❑ b. I am the source of my salvation when I work hard enough to deserve it.

No one will be able to boast about securing his or her own salvation. It comes through faith (13a) and from God alone (14a). Some spiritual leaders and even some religious groups define salvation differently so that members will be "encouraged" to do the right things. God, however, is the only One who has the right to determine the requirements. He has made those requirements clear in the Bible.

Salvation by grace through faith separates true Christianity from all other religions, including all cults and "isms" that are deviations from biblical Christianity. Without exception, all teach salvation by works or a combination of faith and works.

Have you ever presented the gospel to someone who has responded by saying that all religions are basically the same? God says that people are saved by His grace through faith, not by works. Other religions teach that we are saved by works or by faith plus works. A person who has been exposed to the majority of religions in the world will see the similarities with biblical Christianity. Unfortunately, he or she may not un-

---

*Margin notes:*

♦ **saved:** given eternal salvation, delivered, made whole.

♦ **faith:** reliance upon Christ for salvation, trust.

♦ **gift:** a present, something given freely.

♦ **works:** acts, deeds, activities, actions.

♦ **boast:** claim credit, take glory for self.

Salvation by grace through faith separates true Christianity from all other religions.

**Titus 3:4-8**

"When the kindness and love of God our Savior appeared, he saved us, not because of righteous things we had done, but because of his mercy. He saved us through the washing of rebirth and renewal by the Holy Spirit, whom he poured out on us generously through Jesus Christ our Savior, so that, having been justified by his grace, we might become heirs having the hope of eternal life. This is a trustworthy saying. And I want you to stress these things, so that those who have trusted in God may be careful to devote themselves to doing what is good. These things are excellent and profitable for everyone."

derstand this basic truth about true Christianity—salvation comes by faith alone in Christ alone. Paul described the same way of salvation in his letter to Titus. As a review of God's saving grace, let's look at this description.

▶15. **Read Titus 3:4-8 in the margin, and circle the following words:**
   • kindness • love • mercy • grace • hope

▶16. **What are three reasons God saved us? Check them.**
   ❑ a. Because of the righteous things we have done.
   ❑ b. Because of God's kindness.
   ❑ c. Because of God's love.
   ❑ d. Because of God's mercy.

▶17. **In Titus 3:4-8 in the margin, underline the words** *doing what is good.* **When does a person do what is good? Check one.**
   ❑ a. Before trusting in God for salvation.
   ❑ b. After trusting in God for salvation.

God saved us because of His kindness, love, and mercy. Before salvation, you were still "dead in your transgressions and sins" (Eph. 2:1). You were never capable of doing anything that could bring you from death to life. That's where God's resurrection power worked to provide your salvation through Jesus Christ. Your good works come after your salvation as an expression of your love for God and because of His grace (18b).

Paul made very clear where good works fit into the Christian life: "We are God's workmanship, created in Christ Jesus to do good works, which God prepared in advance for us to do" (Eph. 2:10). This is God's plan to reveal His glory through His redeemed creation. But even the ability to do good works is an evidence of God's grace. The Holy Spirit in a believer is the One who enables him or her to do good works. Thus, we are saved by grace, and only by God's grace can we do the good works He desires.

▶18. **Number the items in the order they appear in a person's life. Write 1 for the first and 4 for the last.**

   \_\_\_\_ good works            \_\_\_\_ salvation and new life
   \_\_\_\_ dead in sin           \_\_\_\_ faith in Christ
   (Check your answers: 1-dead in sin; 2-faith; 3-salvation; 4-good works.)

God made it clear that true faith produces good works. James wrote, "Faith without deeds is dead" (James 2:26). If you are truly saved, God's grace through the Holy Spirit in you will help you become like Jesus. You will reflect His glory!

 **Turn to the Lord in prayer.**
   • Thank God for new life and for His grace.
   • Ask Him to continue cleansing and purifying your life to be like Jesus in every way.
   • Worship Him for the glory He reveals in the lives of Christians you know who look like Jesus.
   • Ask Him to help you have boldness to share the message about His grace with those who need His salvation.

## PART 4: RESPONDING TO GOD'S GRACE

**The Shantung Revival**

In the 1920s in the Shantung Province of China, missionaries became concerned because the Christians were acting more like the rest of the world than like Christ. Marie Monsen, a missionary from Norway, began asking people two questions. First, "Have you been born of the Spirit?" Church members would respond that they had. Then she asked, "What evidence do you have of the new birth?" That's a hard question, but it's a fair one. Paul said to the Corinthians, "If anyone is in Christ, he is a new creation; the old has gone, the new has come!" (2 Cor. 5:17). Those who have been saved should be different from those who have not.

God's Spirit began to convict many that they had never really been saved. Their lives had never been changed. They saw no spiritual power or fruit of the Spirit. One missionary realized she had been trusting in her church membership, and she turned to Christ and was saved. A Chinese evangelist realized he had been trusting in his good works, "serving the Lord." He, too, turned to Christ and was saved by grace!

As God began to change lives, unbelievers noticed the difference. They saw God's power and the fruit of God's Spirit in the Christians. Many people turned to Christ in faith, and they, too, experienced God's grace.

**Examine Yourself.** Paul recommended that the Christians in Corinth examine themselves: "Examine yourselves to see whether you are in the faith; test yourselves. Do you not realize that Christ Jesus is in you—unless, of course, you fail the test?" (2 Cor. 13:5).

EVIDENCE OF GOD'S SAVING
GRACE IN MY LIFE

_____

_____

_____

_____

_____

_____

_____

_____

_____

_____

_____

►**19. Have you been born of the Spirit? What's the evidence of this new birth? As you reflect on the following questions, ask the Holy Spirit to reveal to you your position in Christ. After reading the questions and scriptures, you may want to begin making a list of evidence that your life is changed by God's grace. Write notes in the margin.**

- Am I a new creation, where my old sinful way of life is gone? "If anyone is in Christ, he is a new creation; the old has gone, the new has come!" (2 Cor. 5:17).
- Is the Holy Spirit helping me to know I'm a child of God? "The Spirit himself testifies with our spirit that we are God's children" (Rom. 8:16).
- Is the Holy Spirit living in me? "You, however, are controlled not by the sinful nature but by the Spirit, if the Spirit of God lives in you. And if anyone does not have the Spirit of Christ, he does not belong to Christ" (Rom. 8:9).
- Does my life reflect the fruit of the Holy Spirit who dwells in me? "The fruit of the Spirit is love, joy, peace, patience, kindness, goodness, faithfulness, gentleness and self-control. Against such things there is no law. Those who belong to Christ Jesus have crucified the sinful nature with its passions and desires" (Gal. 5:22-24).
- Do I demonstrate love for other believers? "By this all men will know that you are my disciples, if you love one another" (John 13:35). "We know that we have passed from death to life, because we love our brothers. Anyone who does not love remains in death" (1 John 3:14).
- Am I growing in my freedom from sin and victory over temptation? "No one who lives in him keeps on sinning. No one who continues to sin has either seen him or known him" (1 John 3:6).
- Do my deeds show that I have repented of (turned away from) my sin and to God for salvation? "I preached that they should repent and turn to God and prove their repentance by their deeds" (Acts 26:20).

Have you been born again? To help you think more deeply about this question, consider for a moment my (Gene's) experience with the police officer. I was totally surprised when he informed me that I was guilty of violating four laws. I actually thought I was keeping the law. In fact, I felt rather self-righteous as I was driving alongside the squad car. The fact that I thought I wasn't breaking the law, however, did not mean I wasn't guilty. Furthermore, in one instance I was ignorant of the law—the actual speed limit on the service road. But I was guilty nevertheless. You see, ignorance of the law is no excuse!

The same situation applies to millions of people today who are violating God's laws. Some feel they are doing a good job keeping the Ten Commandments or being a "good person." They actually believe they're righteous before God. However, the Bible teaches that if we violate just one commandment, we're just as guilty as if we violated all of them (James 2:10-11). God is just and must punish sin. That's why Jesus Christ came as the perfect Son of God and took our sins upon Himself at the cross.

So, if you're trying to get to heaven by keeping the law or doing good works, you'll never make it. No one except Jesus Christ kept the law perfectly. That's why He was the perfect Savior. The only way to have eternal life is to acknowledge your sin and receive Jesus Christ as personal Savior, and with Him the free gift of salvation.

➤20. Describe in your own words the one way to be saved and have eternal life.

_____

_____

**Don't Reject His Grace.** The police officer did not write out a ticket when he caught me breaking those four laws. Suppose I had responded by saying, "Sir, I'm not going to accept your offer of freedom. I'm guilty of breaking the law. Book me! Fine me! Put me behind bars!" I'm sure you'll agree I would have been foolish to reject his grace. It wouldn't make sense. But neither does it make sense to reject God's offer of salvation. And yet, millions of people are responding to the gospel by saying, "Bring judgment on me; make me pay for my sins; put me behind bars—forever!"

True, many people are not aware of the plan of salvation. They don't understand that the gift is free. But many do know the truth yet refuse to respond positively to God's offer. This, of course, is a foolish decision.

If you know the truth—and if you've read to this point, you certainly do—don't force God to bring judgment on you. Accept His free gift of salvation. As the Bible states, "Today, if you hear his voice, do not harden your hearts" (Heb. 4:7).

 **You may have studied to this point and only now realize you've been trusting in works, the church, or something else for salvation. If you have any doubts about your saving relationship with God, talk to Him about it right now. His Spirit can help you know whether you've been saved by grace. If you now realize you need to place your trust in Christ alone, review Parts 2 and 3 in the introduction (pp. 8-13). Then turn in faith to God and receive His free gift of salvation.**

 **If you already have received God's grace through faith in Christ, thank the Lord for your salvation. Take a few moments to pray for those you know who may need to turn to Him for grace. Ask Him to draw them to Himself. List below the names of any for whom you are praying.**

_____

 **Close this week's lesson by reading Paul's words to Titus in the margin. Ask the Lord to help you live a life pleasing to Him.**

**James 2:10-11**
"For whoever keeps the whole law and yet stumbles at just one point is guilty of breaking all of it. . . . you have become a law-breaker."

**Titus 2:11-14**
"For the grace of God that brings salvation has appeared to all men. It teaches us to say 'No' to ungodliness and worldly passions, and to live self-controlled, upright and godly lives in this present age, while we wait for the blessed hope—the glorious appearing of our great God and Savior, Jesus Christ, who gave himself for us to redeem us from all wickedness and to purify for himself a people that are his very own, eager to do what is good."

# MINICHURCH MEETING 8

## BEFORE THE MEETING

❑ 1. Turn to "Preparing for Your Minichurch Meeting" on page 143. Use it as a guide to get ready for this meeting. Check the box above after you have prepared.

❑ 2. Unless God should direct otherwise, your minichurch leader will be using the following outline to guide your meeting. You may want to look over the questions and activities so you will be better prepared to participate.

## DURING THE MEETING

### ❖ Opening Prayer

### ❖ Singing Together

Consider singing "Grace Greater Than Our Sin," "Amazing Grace," or "At Calvary" together with other choruses and hymns.

### ❖ Building Relationships

The lesson began with Gene's testimony about a policeman's grace. Relate one experience when you received grace from another person, official, or group—a time when you were forgiven when you should have gotten in trouble. Or describe an experience where you wanted and needed grace but you got what you deserved instead.

### ❖ Praying for One Another (in fours or sixes)

Turning to one person at a time, ask, "How can we pray for you?" Focus your prayer requests primarily on spiritual or emotional needs rather than on impersonal or physical needs (unless the physical need is significant at this time). After a person makes his or her request, one or two people should pray. Then ask another person, and pray for that individual.

### ❖ Interacting with the Scriptures (in fours or sixes)

1. What verse or passage of Scripture has been most meaningful or challenging to you this week? How has God used it to speak to you? What significant actions have you taken this week because of something God revealed through His Word?

2. (p. 86) Volunteers: Recite the memory verse you learned this week, and explain any special meaning you gained from it.

3. (p. 86, #5) What word or phrase from Ephesians 2:1-10 have you come to better understand or experience this week? Describe your understanding or experience.

### ❖ Reviewing the Lesson

1. (p. 87, #6) According to Ephesians 2:1-10, what are the characteristics of those who have come to faith in Jesus, and what were their characteristics before salvation?

2. (p. 88) What are three reasons God made His grace available to all humanity? How would you describe or explain each reason?

3. (p. 89, #11) What reasons have you heard given for salvation? Give a few examples.

4. What's necessary to receive God's grace? What's not acceptable for salvation?

5. What's the difference between mercy and grace?

### ❖ Applying the Truths to Life

1. (p. 90, #18) When do good works begin to appear in a person's life?

2. (p. 91) Review the story of the Shantung Revival. What are some evidences in churches today that many people may never have experienced genuine conversion and salvation? How different from the rest of the world are the people you know who claim to be Christians?

2. (p. 91, #19) What evidences are described in the Bible that would indicate a person has genuinely been converted (born again)?

3. (p. 91, margin) What are some of the evidences in your own life that God has, indeed, done a work of saving grace in you? (This shouldn't be a matter of pride or arrogance but a testimony of God's power and goodness. Relate these evidences in a way that points the credit and glory to Him.)

4. (p. 92, #20) How did you describe the one way a person can be saved and have eternal life? Are your descriptions based on Scripture rather than on personal opinion or experience?

### ❖ Responding to God in Prayer

1. Thank God for the way He has worked in your lives. Thank Him for His kindness, love, mercy, and grace.

2. Thank God for others in your minichurch and for the evidences you see in their lives that God has been at work there.

### ❖ Ministering to One Another

What needs (if any) of members have you become aware of during this meeting that the Body needs to care for? What can we do to meet the needs or to help connect the person with those who can help? Are there things we need to do this week to help?

### ❖ Reaching Out to Others

Are there people in your circles of influence who need a saving relationship with Jesus Christ and for whom God seems to be giving you a special burden? What names did you write on the bottom of page 92? What can we pray or do to help you carry that burden?

### ❖ Closing Prayer
### ❖ Optional: "Breaking Bread" Together

93

# LESSON 9
# EXPERIENCING ONENESS IN CHRIST

**From Code of Blood to Unity**

In 1996, I (Claude) was speaking to missionary leaders in Europe. One man was serving in Slovenia (near Bosnia and Serbia). That whole region is filled with ethnic conflict. Murder, genocide, and war have been commonplace for many years. This missionary told me that the people there live by a "code of blood." If a person, family, or ethnic group harms another, the offended party has an obligation to get even. Usually the punishment of the offender is more serious than the original offense. Then that person or group decides it has to seek revenge. The cycle of violence and bitterness has grown over the generations until there seems to be no hope of solving the problems. My missionary friend faced a major difficulty in trying to teach forgiveness. This people group didn't even have a word for "reconciliation" in their language. It was unthinkable that a person would ever forgive another and enter a time of peace and harmony.

Ethnic prejudice and violence are common in nearly every country and culture. Probably no other problem reveals more clearly the depth of human wickedness.

On this same missions trip, I went to Albania, a small country in the region. For some 50 years, Albania had been an atheistic state. It had been illegal to practice a religious faith of any kind. In the early 1990s, however, a new government took control and Christian missionaries were permitted into the country. When I arrived, I was told that more than 600 Christian missionaries from 76 denominations or groups were serving in this small country. I knew God was up to something, because I couldn't imagine anyone wanting to live and serve in Albania unless God called them there.

As I traveled around the country meeting with Christian groups, I was amazed by the tremendous unity I saw. Denominational names didn't seem to be important. The missionaries worked together. They ate and traveled together. They worked on joint projects and sought to share whatever they had with others who had needs. This unity was far different from what I was accustomed to seeing. This was a region where the apostle Paul had started churches in the first century. I began to sense that this unity was much like that of the early church where they had "one mind" and "one heart."

I prayed and asked the Lord what was different about these Christians in Albania. I began to see one factor: Every group was dealing with the very basic message of the gospel. Most people hadn't even heard the name of Jesus for 50 years. When the different groups focused on the heart of the gospel, there was great unity. They desperately wanted to see this pagan nation come to know Jesus Christ as Savior. Then I remembered Jesus' prayer in John 17:23: "May they be brought to complete unity to let the world know that you sent me." Surrounded by a culture that taught a code of blood and vengeance, I saw why unity is such an important quality for God's people. The lost world will notice the difference when they see Godlike unity and love between people who normally can't get along with each other and even kill each other. In this week's lesson, we'll see how God can establish that kind of oneness between people who are very different. When He does that, the church grows strong and God gets glory.

> Surrounded by a culture that taught a code of blood and vengeance, I saw why unity is such an important quality for God's people.

## PART 1: INTERACTING WITH THE SCRIPTURES

### Reading / Hearing God's Word

**Read or Listen to:**

❑ Ephesians 1–6

❑ Ephesians 1–3

❑ Ephesians 2:1-22

➤1. Select one of the reading (or listening) options in the margin. Using your Bible, read or listen to the passage of Scripture. As you begin, ask God to speak to you through His Word. Watch for one verse or idea that's especially meaningful to you. Once you finish reading, check the box indicating the passage you read.

### Meditating on God's Word

**Meaningful Verse or Idea**

_____

_____

_____

➤2. In the margin, write a brief summary of the meaningful verse or idea you just identified.

### Memorizing God's Word

➤3. Select and tear out a new Scripture memory card from the back of your book, or continue reviewing the one you started learning earlier. For a new verse, use the tips for memorizing Scripture on your bookmark.

### Understanding God's Word

♦ **Gentiles:** non-Jews, pagans, heathen.

♦ **uncircumcised:** not circumcised according to the covenant God made with Abraham and his descendants, figuratively unregenerate, a derogatory name for Gentiles.

♦ **circumcision:** people who prided themselves in following the religious ritual (given by God to Abraham) of removing the foreskin of all males.

♦ **separate:** without, apart from, no relationship to.

♦ **Israel:** descendants of Israel (Jacob), the nation chosen by God to be His people.

♦ **covenants of the promise:** God's commitments to Abraham and the patriarchs to bless the world through their descendants by sending a Savior.

♦ **without hope:** no knowledge or expectation of salvation beyond this life.

♦ **peace:** set at one, whole, the One bringing two parts together in oneness.

♦ **dividing wall of hostility:** fence, enclosing barrier, partition, the Mosaic regulations that kept Jews separate from Gentiles.

➤4. Read again the focal passage for this week's lesson (Eph. 2:11-22) below. Underline any key phrases or ideas that seem especially meaningful to you. Then read the brief definitions of key words in the margin on these two facing pages. This will prepare you for the remainder of this week's study.

> **Ephesians 2:11-22**—"Therefore, remember that formerly you who are Gentiles by birth and called 'uncircumcised' by those who call themselves 'the circumcision' (that done in the body by the hands of men)— remember that at that time you were separate from Christ, excluded from citizenship in Israel and foreigners to the covenants of the promise, without hope and without God in the world. But now in Christ Jesus you who once were far away have been brought near through the blood of Christ.

> "For he himself is our peace, who has made the two one and has destroyed the barrier, the dividing wall of hostility, by abolishing in his flesh the law with its commandments and regulations. His purpose was to create in himself one new man out of the two, thus making peace, and in this one body to reconcile both of them to God through the cross, by which he put to death their hostility. He came and preached peace to you who were far away and peace to those who were near. For through him we both have access to the Father by one Spirit.

> "Consequently, you are no longer foreigners and aliens, but fellow citizens with God's people and members of God's household, built on the foundation of the apostles and prophets, with Christ Jesus himself as the chief cornerstone. In him the whole building is joined together and rises to become a holy temple in the Lord. And in him you too are being built together to become a dwelling in which God lives by his Spirit."

➤5. Look back through the list of words in the margins. Circle one that you would like to understand or experience more fully.

### Looking through the Scripture to God

 **Now pause to pray.**

• Ask the Lord to help you understand and remember what you were before He reconciled you to Himself through the cross.

♦ **law:** commands and regulations given by God to Moses and Israel.

♦ **one new man:** a new creation, a new humanity including Jew and Gentile and all races in a mystical new Body of Christ.

♦ **reconcile:** restore to right relationship, removal of offending sin.

♦ **preached:** proclaimed good news.

♦ **citizen:** native of the same town, co-religionist, one who has a home alongside others in a holy nation.

♦ **God's household:** a relative, member of the family, children with one Father.

♦ **apostle:** messenger, one who is sent, an ambassador of the gospel, usually refers to the 12 disciples who had been close to Jesus throughout His ministry and later Paul, by special call of Christ.

♦ **prophets:** foreteller, inspired speaker, one who brought God's messages to His people.

♦ **chief cornerstone:** foundation stone placed at the corner around which a building is constructed.

♦ **holy temple:** the inner sanctuary where God dwells, a spiritual building.

• Ask the Lord to reveal to you any people or groups with whom you have built walls to separate yourself from other members of the Body of Christ.

• Ask Him to help you understand what oneness and unity in the Body of Christ would look like.

• Ask Him to guide you and your group in living out the reality of the unity Christ already has provided.

• Ask the Lord to reveal His great power to the world around you by establishing love and unity between all Christians of different ethnic and denominational groups.

• Ask the Lord to establish unity in your own local church.

• Close by praying Ephesians 1:17-19 and 3:16-19 (on your bookmark) for yourself and your minichurch.

## PART 2: THE PROBLEM WITH PRIDE AND PREJUDICE

All of us at some point have been guilty of prejudice. Prejudice is looking down on other people or groups and thinking we are better. Our elevated opinion of ourselves might be related to social class and economics. It might reflect religious attitudes. It might be due to racial or ethnic origin. In fact, most, if not all, of us have elements of prejudice and pride that we don't even recognize in ourselves.

➤ 6. **Which of the following groups have you ever had some form of prejudice toward, where you looked down on them and kept yourself separate from them? Check all that apply.**

| | | |
|---|---|---|
| ❏ Whites | ❏ Jews | ❏ well educated |
| ❏ Blacks | ❏ Arabs | ❏ uneducated |
| ❏ Hispanics | ❏ Iraqis | ❏ charismatics |
| ❏ Native Americans | ❏ Iranians | ❏ evangelicals |
| ❏ Japanese | ❏ rich | ❏ Pentecostals |
| ❏ Germans | ❏ poor | ❏ Protestants |
| ❏ Asians | ❏ Republicans | ❏ fundamentalists |
| ❏ Italians | ❏ Democrats | ❏ liberals |

Others: _____

No prejudice has ever run deeper, reflected more hostility, and lasted longer than that which has permeated Jewish and Gentile communities through the centuries. Emotions have often run high on both sides, and they still do in many parts of the world. Mutual hostility and resentment are obvious. The strife in the Middle East today is just a continuation of this hatred and hostility between Jews and non-Jews. This week's lesson presents God's peace plan for the Middle East—His peace plan for every human conflict in the world.

**Gentiles by Birth.** Paul dealt with the reality of this deep racial and religious prejudice. Writing first to believing Gentiles, he reminded them of their status before they put their faith in Jesus Christ. They were "Gentiles by birth." Gentiles have their origin in Adam and, after the Flood, in Noah. After Noah and the Flood, people once again turned against God. "Although they knew God, they neither glorified him as God nor gave thanks to him, but their thinking became futile and their foolish hearts were darkened" (Rom. 1:21).

In His mercy, God did not turn His back on mankind, though all people had turned their backs on Him. God reached down in love and chose first a man (Abraham) and

God's ultimate plan was that "all peoples on earth" would "be blessed" through Abraham's seed. That seed was Jesus Christ.

then a nation (Israel) to whom He wanted to reveal His love and through whom He would draw many people back to Himself. He made a covenant with Abraham. God's ultimate plan was that "all peoples on earth" would "be blessed" through Abraham's seed (Gen. 12:1-3). That seed was Jesus Christ. God was preparing for redemption.

The Jews have their origin in Abraham. They were first called "Hebrews." Later, they were called "Israelites," after God changed Jacob's name to Israel. Following the Babylonian captivity, the title "Jew" (originally used to describe the tribe of Judah) was used of all Israel. Generally, the term "Israel" was used to refer to these people as a nation, whereas the term "Jew" was used to designate the people themselves. The same is true today.

➤7. **Write the name of the group beside the definition below.**

_____ 1. Descendants of Abraham through Isaac and Jacob or Israel. The people of Israel.

_____ 2. Descendants of Adam and Noah who turned their backs on God and became pagans.

♦ **circumcision:** people who prided themselves in following the religious ritual (given by God to Abraham) of removing the foreskin of all males.

♦ **uncircumcised:** not circumcised according to the covenant God made with Abraham and his descendants, figuratively unregenerate, a derogatory name for Gentiles.

**Uncircumcised.** When Abraham was 99 years old, God confirmed the eternal covenant of circumcision that He had made with this servant years earlier. God said, "Every male among you shall be circumcised" (Gen. 17:10). And the Lord made it clear that this "sign of the covenant" (Gen. 17:11) should be practiced for "generations to come" (Gen. 17:12). The Gentiles were an uncircumcised people. They didn't belong to the covenant people.

Through the years, circumcision became the distinguishing factor between Jews and Gentiles. Thus, Paul wrote that "Gentiles by birth" were "called 'uncircumcised' by those who call themselves 'the circumcision'" (Eph. 2:11). And to make sure that his readers knew he was talking about the physical act of circumcision, not just a spiritual idea, Paul added, "that done in the body by hands of men" (Eph. 2:11).

➤8. **Today, what are some ways that the "haves" look down on others who "have not"? Check the ones you've seen or experienced. If you can think of others, write them in the margin.**

❑ preferred skin color, race          ❑ right doctrine
❑ education                           ❑ gifts of the Spirit
❑ money, material things              ❑ genealogy, family heritage

**Before Christ.** Paul's readers were uncircumcised, believing Gentiles. Paul next asked his readers to "remember" their former status as unbelieving Gentiles.

**Ephesians 2:12**
"Remember that at that time you were separate from Christ, excluded from citizenship in Israel and foreigners to the covenants of the promise, without hope and without God in the world."

➤9. **Read Ephesians 2:12 in the margin, and underline the five phrases Paul used to describe the status of these Gentiles before Christ. We've underlined one for you.**

Before they came to Christ, they were "separate," "excluded," and "foreigners," "without hope" and "without God." These Gentiles lived in hostility to the Jews. The Jews despised and kept themselves separate from them. Paul wasn't saying that Gentiles could not come to know God.

**Pride and Prejudice.** Even Abraham was a pagan before he encountered God. He, too, worshiped false gods. But the true God chose this man out of his paganism to be a means to provide salvation for those who would respond to His love and grace. The nation Israel was to be a witness of God's righteousness in this world. Unfortunately, for the most part they failed to fulfill this commission. Because of their pride and arrogance, they separated themselves from those to whom God wanted them to carry His light and message. And so the great majority of Gentiles continued in their lost condition before Christ came.

➤ **10. How does having prejudices pose a serious problem for God's people? Check your response or write your own.**

   ❑ a. Prejudice isn't a problem for God's people. God just made some of us better than the rest.

   ❑ b. Prejudice keeps us from carrying out His command to make disciples of all peoples and nations.

   ❑ c. An attitude of superiority could hinder a person from wanting to know the God I serve.

   ❑ d. Both *b* and *c*.

Too many people, even Christians, live as though *a* were true. For the Jews, the greatest problem with their prejudice was the way they kept their relationship with God to themselves. They didn't share it. Probably, from the Gentile's viewpoint, *c* could be true as well. Prejudice is a serious problem for God's people.

Being a Jew by birth did not make God's chosen people true believers. In fact, when Christ came, the great majority of Jews were also unbelievers. Though they believed in God, claimed to keep the law, and were even circumcised, they weren't God's children spiritually. Paul made this clear when he wrote, "A man is not a Jew if he is only one outwardly, nor is circumcision merely outward and physical. No, a man is a Jew if he is one inwardly; and circumcision is circumcision of the heart, by the Spirit, not by the written code. Such a man's praise is not from men, but from God" (Rom. 2:28-29).

The same can be said of people who claim to be Christians. They claim to follow Christ and have even been baptized. However, many have not really been born again by God's Spirit. Their Christianity is purely a ritual they go through. They belong to the institutional church, but they don't belong to Christ. They're practicing "*church*ianity," not Christianity.

> They belong to the institutional church, but they don't belong to Christ. They're practicing "*church*ianity," not Christianity.

➤ **11. Have you ever known a person who claimed to be a Christian and was active in church, but his life gave no indication that he really was born again by God's Spirit?** ❑ Yes ❑ No **If yes, write his or her initials here:** _____

As we've seen, prejudice and its reflection through pride have been a problem even among the people God chose to represent Him on earth. What about you and me? As I (Gene) reflect on my own background, I can see how prejudiced I had become because of what I had been taught from childhood. I'd grown up in a restrictive and legalistic religious community. I also can see that part of that prejudice was ethnic. For years I had been taught that I was better than other people because of my heritage. All other people who called themselves "Christian" were wrong. I had the truth. No one else did.

➤ **12. How would you describe your own background related to prejudice? Check your response or write your own.**

   ❑ a. I was like Gene and had been taught some subtle and even some strong prejudices.

   ❑ b. Though I'm sure there were some subtle prejudices, for the most part I accepted other people and didn't look down on them.

   ❑ c. I was affected even more by the prejudiced way other people treated me.

   ❑ d. Other: _____

Though I (Gene) rejected those attitudes after I became a true Christian, I didn't realize at first how ingrained they were in me. Those prejudiced feelings lingered in my heart. I can see now that God used some disillusioning experiences in my life to help me break out of my narrow and subtle prejudice. In fact, it was only as I was "reaching up to touch bottom" in my spiritual and emotional life that I truly realized how much I needed other people who were not from my own religious and ethnic background.

We must deal with prejudice and pride if we're going to be true to God's Word and walk in His will. All of us struggle with this problem at some level. We must realize that it is only by God's grace that we are what we are. Truly, "God does not show favoritism" (Acts 10:34), and neither should we (James 2:1).

▶ **13. How would you describe your present victory or lack of victory over thoughts and feelings of prejudice? Check your response.**
  ❏ a. I'm not perfect, but mostly God has freed me from prejudice.
  ❏ b. From time to time, I still have to deal with prejudiced attitudes.
  ❏ c. I'd have to confess that I'm a very prejudiced person. I need the Lord's help.
  ❏ d. I'm very prejudiced, but I don't see any need to change.

Because of our humanity, we will continue to need God's help in dealing with pride and prejudice. He can help us live on the victory side.

 **Thank God that He didn't reject you because you didn't measure up to His standards. Thank Him for the work you already see of His grace regarding the removal of prejudice. Ask Him to continue His work in you. If you don't sense a need to deal with pride and prejudice, ask God to reveal His will to you in this matter.**

## PART 3: GOD'S PROVISION FOR ONENESS

When you think about human conflict around the world, the idea of oneness between groups so different seems impossible. The truth is that oneness *is* impossible apart from Christ. God chose to demonstrate His mighty power to produce oneness between Jew and Gentile when He sent His Son to the cross.

▶ **14. Read Ephesians 2:14-18 in the margin, and answer these questions.**

  1. (v. 14) Who removed the dividing wall of hostility? _____

  2. (v. 15) What was His purpose?

  _____

  3. (v. 16) How did He put to death their hostility?

  _____

  4. (vv. 15-16) In what would their unity be revealed? "in this one . . ."

  _____

Christ removed the dividing wall. He did everything necessary to provide oneness. His purpose was to make them one new man as the Body of Christ—the church—and thus bring peace. By His death on the cross, Christ reconciled them to God. This oneness would be revealed to a watching world. What Christ made possible for Jews and Gentiles, He also made possible for blacks and whites, for Bosnians and Serbs, and for every other pair of people groups that are living in prejudice and conflict. God's greatest glory is revealed when those who are so divided become one in Christ!

---

*Margin notes:*

**James 2:1**
"My brothers, as believers in our glorious Lord Jesus Christ, don't show favoritism."

**Ephesians 2:14-18**
[14]"For he himself is our peace, who has made the two one and has destroyed the barrier, the dividing wall of hostility, [15]by abolishing in his flesh the law with its commandments and regulations. His purpose was to create in himself one new man out of the two, thus making peace, [16]and in this one body to reconcile both of them to God through the cross, by which he put to death their hostility. [17]He came and preached peace to you who were far away and peace to those who were near. [18]For through him we both have access to the Father by one Spirit."

*God's greatest glory is revealed when those who are divided become one in Christ!*

The night before going to the cross, Jesus spent time giving His disciples some last-minute instructions. Then He prayed His high priestly prayer in John 17. In it, He explained why oneness and unity would be so important to His redemptive purposes.

▶ **15. Read John 17:21, 23, and underline the reason Jesus gave for asking that His followers be brought together in complete unity.**

> "Father, just as you are in me and I am in you. May they also be in us so that the world may believe that you have sent me. . . . May they be brought to complete unity to let the world know that you sent me and have loved them even as you have loved me" (John 17:21, 23).

> *Jesus knew that the unity of His followers would reveal most clearly to a watching world that He was, indeed, the divine Son of God and the Savior of the world.*

Jesus knew that the unity of His followers would reveal most clearly to a watching world that He was, indeed, the divine Son of God and the Savior of the world. The oneness He shared with the Father is the same oneness He desires for us. Jesus died on the cross to reconcile us to God and make peace between all the people He places in the Body of Christ.

In recent years, God has allowed our nation to finally realize that society doesn't have a solution to race problems. Government can do some things that help, but the root problem is in the human heart. Only Christ can change the hearts of very different people in such a way that they can live together in harmony and love. Now is a time God is calling Christians to live in the reality of the oneness He provided on the cross.

For many churches, however, racism is not the greatest problem. They can't even get along with brothers and sisters in Christ who are much more like them than different. Such sin in the Body of Christ brings shame and discredit to His name. Our lack of unity is saying to the world, "Jesus couldn't possibly be God or else He could make us one." In the final part of our lesson, we'll look at how we can experience the oneness Christ died to provide.

 Talk to God about your personal experience of oneness in His Body. If unity is lacking, ask God to prepare you to receive the next part of the lesson. Ask Him to move your life, your church, and all His people toward oneness so a lost world will come to know Him.

## PART 4: EXPERIENCING THE REALITY OF OUR ONENESS

**Oneness in the Body.** Paul described the unity as "one new man" in one "body." This is the Body of Christ. In 1 Corinthians 12 and Romans 12, Paul described the church as the Body of Christ. There are many members but one body, and Jesus Christ is the head.

> **1 Corinthians 12:12, 24-26**
>
> "The body is a unit, though it is made up of many parts; and though all its parts are many, they form one body. So it is with Christ. . . .
>
> "But God has combined the members of the body . . . so that there should be no division in the body, but that its parts should have equal concern for each other. If one part suffers, every part suffers with it; if one part is honored, every part rejoices with it."

I (Claude) spoke to a group of about 500 ethnic pastors meeting in the annual convention of their denomination. In a meeting with the leaders beforehand, they said I needed to understand that they had bad tempers. On the side, one of the men explained that three different years their guest speaker didn't get to speak because the business meeting went too long. They got into such heated debate over their business that they had no time left for the message. Fortunately, I was on the front end of the program this year.

I spoke from John 17 and Ephesians 2–4 about the role of unity in spiritual awakening. Jesus said that our unity was the way a lost world would know He was God's Son. Paul commanded us to "make every effort to keep the unity of the Spirit through the bond of peace" (Eph. 4:3). God's Spirit took God's Word and brought great conviction, because they had no visible unity in their convention.

**Romans 12:3-5, 16**

"Do not think of yourself more highly than you ought, but rather think of yourself with sober judgment, in accordance with the measure of faith God has given you. Just as each of us has one body with many members, and these members do not all have the same function, so in Christ we who are many form one body, and each member belongs to all the others....

"Live in harmony with one another. Do not be proud, but be willing to associate with people of low position. Do not be conceited."

**Galatians 5:22-23**

"The fruit of the Spirit is love, joy, peace, patience, kindness, goodness, faithfulness, gentleness and self-control."

**Romans 6:2, 6-7**

"By no means! We died to sin; how can we live in it any longer?... We should no longer be slaves to sin—because anyone who has died has been freed from sin."

**Ephesians 2:19-22**

"Consequently, you are no longer foreigners and aliens, but fellow citizens with God's people and members of God's household, built on the foundation of the apostles and prophets, with Christ Jesus himself as the chief cornerstone. In him the whole building is joined together and rises to become a holy temple in the Lord. And in him you too are being built together to become a dwelling in which God lives by his Spirit."

Then I spoke about the Body of Christ as a place where we experience the unity Christ provides. In that body, there is only one head—Christ. That means that our opinions don't matter. Only His matters. I explained that when they came to business meetings, they should have one mind and heart to say, "Lord, we don't have any will of our own. We want to know Your will."

Then I addressed the problem of their tempers head-on. I pointed out that a fruit of the Spirit is self-control (Gal. 5:22-23). An out-of-control temper is sin and an evidence that the Spirit is not in control. Then we turned to Romans 6, and I showed them that they have "died to sin" and been set free from slavery to sin. I explained that they didn't have to have a bad temper. They could be set free from it. After speaking, I had to leave.

The next week, I spoke to some of the leaders again. They said, "We started our business meeting the next day. We had such a spirit of unity that we finished in half a day, and we spent the other half of the day praying for each other. Many said it was our most spiritual meeting in our sixteen-year history." Friends, Christ can establish unity in His Body! When He does, there is great joy, love, and peace.

➤ **16. How would you evaluate the experience of unity in your local church? Check your response or write your own.**

❏ a. We are much like this group. We have trouble getting along with one another.

❏ b. We have a history of church divisions and splits. We're not even close to experiencing oneness.

❏ c. By God's grace, we're growing in oneness. People are coming to Christ. We're experiencing the oneness Jesus prayed for in John 17.

❏ d. Other: _____

**Other Illustrations of Oneness.** Paul also gave three more illustrations (word pictures) of unity.

➤ **17. Read Ephesians 2:19-22 in the margin, and circle words or phrases that might give a word picture of our unity in the Body of Christ.**

When God adds us to the Body of Christ, we become "fellow citizens" of a holy nation. In the Old Testament, Israel had 12 tribes. They were different, lived in different areas around the Tabernacle, and maintained their genealogies. God never told them to quit having tribes in order to have unity as one nation under God. But they could experience their oneness under God by worshiping together. And they came together in oneness when they went out to fight against the enemy. The Body of Christ today can function as one holy nation even though there are many different ethnic and denominational "tribes."

Paul also described believers as "members of God's household." Because we're all brothers and sisters in Christ, with the same Father over all, we share a family resemblance. We can function like family with one another. The third illustration of our oneness is as a spiritual building that becomes a holy temple in which God lives.

**Hindrances to Oneness.** Christ did everything necessary for our oneness. When we're not experiencing oneness, it's because of sin.

➤18. **Read the following list of sins. Check the ones that may be hindering the experience of oneness in your church or in your family.**

| | | |
|---|---|---|
| ❑ anger | ❑ critical spirit | ❑ revenge |
| ❑ arrogance | ❑ complaining | ❑ selfish ambition |
| ❑ bitterness | ❑ gossip | ❑ struggle for control |
| ❑ impatience | ❑ slander | ❑ judgmental spirit |
| ❑ unforgivingness | ❑ lies | ❑ spirit of superiority |
| ❑ deception | ❑ faultfinding | ❑ injustice |
| ❑ jealousy | ❑ boasting | ❑ hatred |
| ❑ competition | ❑ arguing | ❑ fits of rage |

Of course, many other sins also can break our fellowship with other believers. But the sins listed above can keep the Body of Christ sick and divided when God intended it to be healthy and united.

God is working in many areas of the Christian life, wanting to restore oneness between those who claim His name. It's important to Him—it cost the life of His Son to provide it. He wants to restore unity in families and churches. He wants Christians of different ethnic backgrounds to live in love and concern for one another to show a lost world the difference Christ can make in lives.

The first step in returning is to agree with God about our sin, repent, and seek His help in living free from that sin. If we've offended others, we need to seek their forgiveness. If we've been holding grudges or bitterness, we need to forgive completely. Then, under God's leadership, we need to live in loving relationship with those God has placed around our lives.

 **In the left margin, we've summarized steps you can take to be restored to the oneness Christ died to provide. Pray through this list. Ask the Lord to guide your response to Him. Ask Him to restore your experience of oneness with your brothers and sisters in Christ.**

**RETURNING TO ONENESS**

1. Confess your sin.

2. Repent and return to God.

3. Live in victory over sin. Don't do it anymore.

4. Seek forgiveness from those you've wronged.

5. Forgive any who have offended you.

6. Live in love.

# MINICHURCH MEETING 9

## BEFORE THE MEETING

❏ 1. Turn to "Preparing for Your Minichurch Meeting" on page 143. Use it as a guide to get ready for this meeting. Check the box above after you have prepared.

❏ 2. Unless God should direct otherwise, your minichurch leader will be using the following outline to guide your meeting. You may want to look over the questions and activities so you will be better prepared to participate.

## DURING THE MEETING

### ❖ Opening Prayer

### ❖ Singing Together

Consider singing "Blest Be the Tie That Binds" or "Christian Hearts, in Love United" together with other choruses and hymns. As special music, you might want to listen to a recording of Steve Green singing "Let the Walls Fall Down."

### ❖ Building Relationships

1. What's one way you have either experienced or practiced prejudice in a way that hurt you and those around you?

2. What (if any) are some of the major prejudices you were taught or learned as a child?

### ❖ Praying for One Another (in fours or sixes)

1. If members have just described some painful experiences, be sensitive to pray for them. Be prepared to pray for forgiveness or healing if either is needed.

2. Volunteers: What's your greatest need related to the oneness we've studied this week? How can we pray for you? (After a person speaks, pray. Then listen to the next volunteer and pray.)

### ❖ Interacting with the Scriptures (in fours or sixes)

1. What verse or passage of Scripture has been most meaningful or challenging to you this week? How has God used it to speak to you? What significant actions have you taken this week because of something God revealed through His Word?

2. (p. 96) Volunteers: Recite the memory verse you learned this week, and explain any special meaning you gained from it.

3. (p. 96, #5) What word or phrase from Ephesians 2:11-22 have you come to better understand or experience this week? Describe your understanding or experience.

### ❖ Reviewing the Lesson

1. (p. 97) What is prejudice?

2. (pp. 98-99) How did pride and prejudice affect God's plan to reach the world through Israel?

3. (pp. 100-101) What has Christ done to provide for our oneness and unity?

4. (p. 101) Why is our unity as disciples important to God's plan of redemption through Christ?

5. (p. 102) What physical illustrations, or word pictures, did Paul use to describe the oneness of God's people?

### ❖ Applying the Truths to Life

1. (p. 98, #8) What are some ways you have seen the "haves" look down on "have nots"?

2. (p. 99, #10) How does having prejudices pose a serious problem for God's people? Discuss your responses.

3. (pp. 99-100) Volunteers: How would you describe your experiences with prejudice? Discuss and explain your responses to #12 and #13.

4. (p. 101) Based on Jesus' prayer in John 17, how important do you think unity is to God? Why?

5. (p. 102, #16) How would you evaluate the unity in our church? What are some recent experiences of our church body that support our responses?

6. (pp. 101-102) What, if any, thoughts from the ethnic pastors' meeting would have application to our church? How can we function more like a body?

7. (p. 103, #18) What sins, if any, seem to be the most prevalent in our church? How can we help each other apply the steps in "Returning to Oneness"?

### ❖ Responding to God in Prayer

1. In the larger group, take turns confessing sin or any ways you have failed to express oneness in your families and congregation. Ask the Lord to forgive you for the way you may have hindered others from coming to know Christ.

2. Ask the Lord to oversee the reconciliation of every member of your church body to Him and to one another.

3. Thank God for what He has done to provide for your oneness. Be specific. Ask Him to guide you to experience oneness in ways that will honor Him and His Son.

### ❖ Ministering to One Another

What needs (if any) of members have you become aware of during this meeting that the Body needs to care for? What can we do to meet the needs or to help connect the person with those who can help? Are there things we need to do this week to help?

### ❖ Reaching Out to Others

Discuss how your unity or lack of it may be contributing to or hindering your ability to reach out to others. Is lack of unity in your families affecting the salvation of family members?

### ❖ Closing Prayer

### ❖ Optional: "Breaking Bread" Together

# LESSON 10
# BEING GOD'S SERVANT

**"Silver or Gold I Do Not Have"**

When I (Claude) was in high school, I developed a real interest in archaeology (the study of past cultures). I collected Indian arrowheads and other artifacts I found on farms in Middle Tennessee. During my senior year, I met key people in the field from the University of Tennessee. They offered me a summer job on a field crew doing excavations in the area.

Of the 19 people in the crew, I was the only professing Christian. Every payday most of the crew would go to Nashville to drink and visit the strip joints on Printer's Alley. I took a good bit of ridicule for not going with them. One day Bruce said, "Claude, when you get to UT this fall, you're going to find out that all this religious stuff is a bunch of bull. You might as well dump it now and have some fun." My last night with the crew, they gave me an award—a fifth of liquor and a pornographic book. When they asked for a speech, I had an opportunity to speak to them about how much my faith meant to me.

**"Here am I. Send me!"**

When I went to college, I knew I needed to get established in a church. I needed to fellowship with other believers to remain strong. The first church I visited seemed like just the right place. I prayed that the Lord would use me there and not let me sit on the sidelines uninvolved. That day, the preacher used Isaiah 6 as his text. God had a special assignment, and Isaiah said, "Here am I. Send me!" (Isa. 6:8). The preacher said, "If God calls you and you volunteer, you'd better be ready to go."

I responded to the invitation and joined the church. The student minister came by and asked, "When do you want to go witnessing with me?" I put him off. That night, I sensed the Lord asking me if I was really serious when I told Him I wanted to be involved. I decided I had better go. As I went with him, I began to wonder if I was supposed to be an archaeologist. Did God want me working with live people instead of dead things?

I had so much going for me in my chosen field that I didn't want to change directions unless I was sure it was what God wanted. One Sunday morning, I was so miserable I said, "Lord, You're going to have to give me some relief. I need to hear something from You to know what to do. Would You please speak to me today?"

A visiting preacher was speaking in the morning service. He explained the unusual circumstances around his invitation to speak. Then he said, "I believe God has called me to speak to someone in particular today."

I said, "Lord, I'm listening."

He told of his work as a missionary and made an appeal for a missions offering. I was so moved that I wanted to give a big offering. But I realized I had only 47 cents in my pocket. I didn't have much more in my bank account. Then I remembered the words of Peter when he was asked for money at the temple gate: "Silver or gold I do not have, but what I have I give you" (Acts 3:6). I was overwhelmed with the sense that God was saying, "Claude, I am not interested in your money. I want your life." I had no idea what He wanted me to do, but that day I surrendered my life to be available as His servant.

**Read or Listen to:**

❑ Ephesians 1–6

❑ Ephesians 1–3

❑ Ephesians 3:1-21

♦ **Gentiles:** non-Jews, pagans, heathen.

♦ **administration:** stewardship, management, oversight of an estate.

♦ **grace:** undeserved favor, free gift of salvation.

♦ **mystery:** a divine secret that has been or is being revealed.

♦ **revelation:** illumination, manifestation, uncovering.

♦ **insight:** knowledge, understanding.

♦ **revealed:** made known, declared.

♦ **apostles:** usually refers to the 12 disciples and later Paul, by special calling of Christ.

♦ **prophet:** foreteller, inspired speaker, one who brought God's messages to His people.

♦ **gospel:** a good message, good news.

♦ **heirs:** those who receive an inheritance.

♦ **sharer:** co-participant, partaker.

♦ **servant:** an attendant, one with menial duties, minister, deacon.

♦ **power:** miraculous force, might, strength.

♦ **preach:** tell good news.

♦ **unsearchable:** past finding out, untraceable.

♦ **discouraged:** faint, weak, weary, failing in heart.

♦ **sufferings:** tribulations, afflictions, burdens, troubles, persecution.

♦ **glory:** evidence of God's wonderful work or character, honor.

## PART 1: INTERACTING WITH THE SCRIPTURES

### Reading / Hearing God's Word

➤1. Select one of the reading (or listening) options in the margin. Using your Bible, read or listen to the passage of Scripture. As you begin, ask God to speak to you through His Word. Watch for one verse or idea that's especially meaningful to you. Once you finish reading, check the box indicating the passage you read.

### Meditating on God's Word

➤2. Write a brief summary below of the meaningful verse or idea you just identified.

_____

_____

### Memorizing God's Word

➤3. Select and tear out a new Scripture memory card from the back of your book, or continue reviewing one you started learning earlier. For a new verse, use the tips for memorizing Scripture on your bookmark.

### Understanding God's Word

➤4. Read again the focal passage for this week's lesson (Eph. 3:1-9, 13) below. Underline any key phrases or ideas that seem especially meaningful to you. Then read the brief definitions of key words in the margin. This will prepare you for the remainder of this week's study.

> **Ephesians 3:1-9, 13**—"For this reason I, Paul, the prisoner of Christ Jesus for the sake of you Gentiles—
>
> "Surely you have heard about the administration of God's grace that was given to me for you, that is, the mystery made known to me by revelation, as I have already written briefly. In reading this, then, you will be able to understand my insight into the mystery of Christ, which was not made known to men in other generations as it has now been revealed by the Spirit to God's holy apostles and prophets. This mystery is that through the gospel the Gentiles are heirs together with Israel, members together of one body, and sharers together in the promise in Christ Jesus.
>
> "I became a servant of this gospel by the gift of God's grace given me through the working of his power. Although I am less than the least of all God's people, this grace was given me: to preach to the Gentiles the unsearchable riches of Christ, and to make plain to everyone the administration of this mystery, which for ages past was kept hidden in God, who created all things. . . . I ask you, therefore, not to be discouraged because of my sufferings for you, which are your glory."

➤5. Look back through this list of words. Circle one that you would like to understand or experience more fully.

### Looking through the Scripture to God

Now pause to pray about this gospel God has made known.

- Thank God that you are an heir, a member of Christ's Body, and a sharer together in the promise in Christ.
- Ask the Lord what role He might have for you as a servant of His.

- Give God permission to guide your life to join Him in His work.
- Ask the Lord if there are any adjustments you need to begin making to be prepared to serve Him in the days ahead.
- Ask the Lord if He has any assignments for you at this point regarding your family, your church, your work, or your community. Ask Him to speak to you this week in any way He chooses.
- Close by praying Ephesians 1:17-19 and 3:16-19 (on your bookmark) for yourself and your minichurch.

## PART 2: PAUL'S CALL TO BE A SERVANT OF CHRIST

In last week's lesson, we learned that God reconciled both Jew and Gentile to Himself through the cross of Christ. Together with believing Jews, God made the believing Gentiles "fellow citizens" of a holy nation. He made them both "members of God's household" (family). And God joined them into a spiritual temple where He "lives by His Spirit" (Eph. 2:16-22). This was really good news to the Gentiles!

➤6. **How do you think the non-Christian Jews felt about Paul's teaching that the Gentiles had access to God just like the Jews? Check one.**
  - ❑ a. The Jews were thrilled that God opened the way for the Gentiles to come to Him. They were proud of Paul's missionary work that carried this good news to the Gentile world.
  - ❑ b. The Jews didn't really care what happened to the Gentiles.
  - ❑ c. The Jews were jealous and hated Paul for encouraging the Gentiles to follow the God of Abraham, Isaac, and Israel (Jacob).

If you checked *c*, you are correct. Paul was not a popular man with the unbelieving Jews. That's why he started chapter 3 by saying, "For this reason I, Paul, the prisoner of Christ Jesus for the sake of you Gentiles . . ." Paul met hostile Jews everywhere he went from the beginning of his ministry. He was stoned, beaten, and imprisoned on a number of occasions. During a visit to Jerusalem, he was falsely accused and arrested. After a series of trials, he appealed to Caesar and was sent to Rome.

Paul's first imprisonment in Rome is described in the last chapter of the Book of Acts. Following a long and eventful journey, he finally arrived in Rome. Because of some unique circumstances, he was allowed to rent a home and live apart from other prisoners. However, he was chained to a Roman guard 24 hours a day (Acts 28:16). Three days after he arrived, Paul "called together the leaders of the Jews" (Acts 28:17). He told them the events that had brought him there. He also pointed them to the Old Testament Scriptures to demonstrate that Jesus Christ was the true Messiah. The response was divided, just as it had been throughout his previous missionary journeys. Some of his fellow Jews responded to the gospel. Others rejected the message.

And once again, after first confronting his own people, he turned to the Gentiles. Thus we read, "For two whole years Paul stayed there in his own rented house and welcomed all who came to see him. Boldly and without hindrance he preached the kingdom of God and taught them about the Lord Jesus Christ" (Acts 28:30-31).

During this time in prison, Paul wrote at least four of his letters. The first was probably Philippians, followed by Colossians and Philemon. The letter to the Ephesians was no doubt written shortly before he was released for a period of time. Paul was imprisoned a second time and was killed at the hands of the wicked Roman emperor Nero.

Why was Paul willing to suffer imprisonment and death for the sake of the Gentiles? The answer (in part) is in Ephesians 3:7—"I became a servant of this gospel by the gift of God's grace given me." Paul was a faithful and obedient servant even in the face of suffering. In this lesson we want to look at what being a servant of God means.

➤7. **During one of his hearings, Paul gave a testimony about his calling and ministry. Turn in your Bible to Acts 26 and read the testimony in verses 4-23. Watch for a reason Paul was willing to suffer for Christ in verse 19. After you've read the passage, write the reason below.**

_____

God used a dramatic experience to call Paul to carry His message to the Gentiles. Paul said, "I was not disobedient to the vision from heaven" (Acts 26:19). A faithful servant is obedient to the assignment God gives. In this week's text, Paul said, "You have heard about the administration of God's grace that was given to me for you" (Eph. 3:2). The word for "administration" refers to a trust given to a household manager or steward. Paul saw his calling as a sacred trust given to him because of God's grace.

➤8. **Using the text for this lesson in the margin, answer these questions:**

1. (vv. 2-5) From where and how did Paul receive this sacred trust?

_____

2. (v. 6) What is the mystery? Fill in the blanks. This mystery is that,

through the gospel the Gentiles are _____ together with Israel,

_____ together of one body, and _____

together in the promise in Christ Jesus.

3. (v. 7) Why did Paul become a "servant of the gospel"?

_____

4. (v. 8) True or false? (Circle one.) Paul knew he was chosen for this assignment because of his talents and abilities. He deserved the job.

5. (v. 13) What good were Paul's sufferings for the sake of the Gentiles?

_____

Paul received this trust from God through divine revelation. It didn't come by human reasoning. The mystery God revealed is that believing Gentiles and Jews are joint heirs, members of one body, and joint sharers in the promise of salvation. Gentiles didn't have to become Jews. In Christ they were made new. This trust was given to Paul because of God's grace. It wasn't deserved. Paul's sufferings for the Gentiles allowed God to bring them to salvation and thus reveal His glory in them.

 **Thank God that because of Paul's faithfulness, God's glory is being revealed in the Body of Christ. Ask the Lord to speak to you in the remainder of this lesson about what it means for you to be His servant.**

---

**Ephesians 3:2-9, 13**

²"Surely you have heard about the administration of God's grace that was given to me for you, ³that is, the mystery made known to me by revelation, as I have already written briefly. ⁴In reading this, then, you will be able to understand my insight into the mystery of Christ, ⁵which was not made known to men in other generations as it has now been revealed by the Spirit to God's holy apostles and prophets. ⁶This mystery is that through the gospel the Gentiles are heirs together with Israel, members together of one body, and sharers together in the promise in Christ Jesus.

⁷"I became a servant of this gospel by the gift of God's grace given me through the working of his power. ⁸Although I am less than the least of all God's people, this grace was given me: to preach to the Gentiles the unsearchable riches of Christ, ⁹and to make plain to everyone the administration of this mystery, which for ages past was kept hidden in God, who created all things. . . . ¹³I ask you, therefore, not to be discouraged because of my sufferings for you, which are your glory."

## PART 3: PRINCIPLES OF SERVANTHOOD

When God calls us to salvation, He calls us to be on a mission with Him. We are His witnesses. He is the master and we are His servants. Paul said, "You, my brothers . . . . serve one another in love. The entire law is summed up in a single command: 'Love your neighbor as yourself'" (Gal. 5:13-14). Jesus also spoke about servanthood to the disciples. He said,

> "You know that the rulers of the Gentiles lord it over them, and their high officials exercise authority over them. Not so with you. Instead, whoever wants to become great among you must be your servant, and whoever wants to be first must be your slave—just as the Son of Man did not come to be served, but to serve, and to give his life as a ransom for many" (Matt. 20:25-28).

Jesus became a servant for our sake and He showed us what being a servant of God would look like. From the teachings of Jesus, Paul, and other New Testament writers, we can learn many basic principles about our role as servants of Christ.

➤9. **Read through the following list of principles and the scriptures that go with them. Underline statements or ideas that seem to be especially meaningful to you. In the margin beside each principle, write a key word or summary phrase of the principle. We've completed the first one for you.**

SUMMARY WORD OR PHRASE

1. <u>Christ alone is Lord</u>

2. _____

3. _____

4. _____

5. _____

6. _____

7. _____

1. **You can't serve two masters. Christ alone must be your Lord.**

   Matthew 6:24—"No one can serve two masters. Either he will hate the one and love the other, or he will be devoted to the one and despise the other. You cannot serve both God and Money."

2. **God is interested in absolute surrender of your will to His.**

   Luke 14:33—"Any of you who does not give up everything he has cannot be my disciple."

3. **You must allow God to mold and shape your life to be prepared for the assignment.**

   Romans 9:20-21—"Who are you, O man, to talk back to God? 'Shall what is formed say to him who formed it, "Why did you make me like this?"' Does not the potter have the right to make out of the same lump of clay some pottery for noble purposes and some for common use?"

4. **You must be humble, not proud.**

   Matthew 23:12—"Whoever exalts himself will be humbled, and whoever humbles himself will be exalted."

5. **You need to be a clean vessel in order to be of most use to God.**

   1 John 3:3— "Everyone who has this hope in him purifies himself, just as he is pure."

6. **Your assignments are God-given, not chosen.**

   John 15:16—"You did not choose me, but I chose you and appointed you to go and bear fruit—fruit that will last."

7. **If you are faithful with a little, God will be able to trust you with more.**

   Matthew 25:21—"His master replied, 'Well done, good and faithful servant! You have been faithful with a few things; I will put you in charge of many things. Come and share your master's happiness!'"

SUMMARY WORD OR PHRASE

8. _____

9. _____

10. _____

11. _____

12. _____

13. _____

14. _____

**8. You must depend on God for the spiritual gift and resources to serve.**

John 15:5—"I am the vine; you are the branches. . . . apart from me you can do nothing."

**9. You work on God's timetable, not your own.**

Matthew 24:45-46—"Who then is the faithful and wise servant, whom the master has put in charge of the servants in his household to give them their food at the proper time? It will be good for that servant whose master finds him doing so when he returns."

**10. You must remain in constant fellowship with God to allow the life of Christ to bear abundant and lasting fruit.**

John 15:5—"I am the vine; you are the branches. If a man remains in me and I in him, he will bear much fruit."

**11. To whom much is given, much is required. You must be faithful with all God has given.**

Luke 12:48—"From everyone who has been given much, much will be demanded."

1 Corinthians 4:2—"Now it is required that those who have been given a trust must prove faithful."

**12. You must be ready to suffer for the cause of Christ. Like Christ, for the joy set before you, you will be able to endure "the cross."**

Luke 9:23—"If anyone would come after me, he must deny himself and take up his cross daily and follow me."

Hebrews 12:2-3—"Let us fix our eyes on Jesus, . . . who for the joy set before him endured the cross . . . . Consider him who endured such opposition from sinful men, so that you will not grow weary and lose heart."

**13. You should seek to win God's approval, not please men.**

Galatians 1:10—"Am I now trying to win the approval of men, or of God? Or am I trying to please men? If I were still trying to please men, I would not be a servant of Christ."

**14. You don't have to claim your rights. You can give up your rights for a higher cause.**

1 Corinthians 9:12—"If others have this right of support from you, shouldn't we have it all the more? But we did not use this right. On the contrary, we put up with anything rather than hinder the gospel of Christ."

1 Corinthians 9:14-15—"The Lord has commanded that those who preach the gospel should receive their living from the gospel. But I have not used any of these rights."

▶10. Now look back over your summary words or phrases in the margin. Which principle do you need to improve on most? Draw a star beside one or two that seem to be principles the Lord would most want you to improve on.

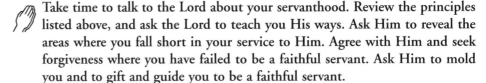 Take time to talk to the Lord about your servanthood. Review the principles listed above, and ask the Lord to teach you His ways. Ask Him to reveal the areas where you fall short in your service to Him. Agree with Him and seek forgiveness where you have failed to be a faithful servant. Ask Him to mold you and to gift and guide you to be a faithful servant.

## PART 4: RESPONDING TO GOD'S CALL TO BE HIS SERVANT

God had such a significant plan to use Paul for carrying the gospel to the Gentiles that He wanted to make sure Paul knew what He desired. The encounter on the road to Damascus was a dramatic calling. Though God could still call a person that way, He's more likely to use less-dramatic ways.

One thing you need to keep in mind is that an assignment from God is God's work. He wants you to know of His assignment more than you do. He's not going to hide it from you. He's not going to make understanding it complicated. He is quite capable of speaking to you in a way that you clearly know the assignment is from Him. You must keep your focus on having the kind of intimate relationship with the Lord where you know His voice and you have a heart to obey. Here are some ways God may reveal an assignment to you:

**1. Through the Scriptures.** God may speak through His Word and then make a mental connection between that Word and a real need or opportunity. Take this thought to the Lord in prayer for a sense of confirmation, with a willingness on the front end to obey whatever you may sense He tells you.

> **Ways God May Reveal Assignments**
> 1. Through the Scriptures
> 2. Through prayer
> 3. Through circumstances
> 4. Through other believers

➤11. **What's one way God may reveal an assignment to you?**

1. Through _____ 3. Through circumstances

2. Through prayer 4. Through other believers

**2. Through Prayer.** God may give you a special burden as you're praying for a person, a group, or a special need. Take the burden to the Lord and ask Him what He would have you do or how He would have you respond. As you're praying, God may impress upon you to pray a certain way for a request, and you may realize that what He guided you to ask is what He wants to do to answer the request.

➤12. **What are two ways God may reveal an assignment to you?**

1. Through _____ 3. Through circumstances

2. Through _____ 4. Through other believers

**3. Through Circumstances.** God may bring to your attention a need or a ministry opportunity as you go through the day. As you examine that opportunity with the teaching of Scripture, you may realize that you need to respond out of love or obedience. You may take the opportunity to the Lord in prayer for confirmation. Sometimes, like the Good Samaritan, you will respond out of love without needing any other reason. If God opens your spiritual eyes to an opportunity or need, that may be His invitation for you to be involved.

➤13. **What are three ways God may reveal an assignment to you?**

1. Through _____ 3. Through _____

2. Through _____ 4. Through other believers

**4. Through Other Believers.** Another believer, your minichurch, or your church may state a need or a service opportunity. The Holy Spirit within you may immediately touch your heart to respond, or He may give you a sense that this is not an assignment for you. As someone has said, "The need does not always constitute a call." When a number of believers seem to come to the same sense of direction independently, you will want to carefully consider that this may be because the head of the Body (Christ) is guiding them. If Christ is guiding the Body, you can trust Him to help the Body come to a common understanding of His will with a spirit of unity.

➤14. What are four ways God may reveal an assignment to you?

1. Through _____ 3. Through _____

2. Through _____ 4. Through _____

➤15. Read the following brief case studies. In which way do you think God revealed the assignment? Write in the blank the number for the way listed in the margin that corresponds with each case study below.

**Ways God May Reveal Assignments**

1. Through the Scriptures
2. Through prayer
3. Through circumstances
4. Through other believers

_____ a. As you're walking down the street, a beggar asks you for a quarter. You walk on by but begin to think about Jesus' statement in the Sermon on the Mount, "Give to the one who asks you, and do not turn away from the one who wants to borrow from you" (Matt. 5:42). You turn around and talk to the man. You find out he's having his shoes repaired and needs money to get them back. You walk around the corner to the shoe shop and pay the bill for his shoes.

_____ b. During your morning Bible reading, you come to Paul's words to Titus, "Teach slaves to be subject to their masters in everything, to try to please them, not to talk back to them, . . . but to show that they can be fully trusted, so that in every way they will make the teaching about God our Savior attractive" (Titus 2:9-10). God convicts you that you haven't been acting that way in your relationship with your boss at work. You ask God to forgive you and to begin teaching you to make the gospel appealing to your boss.

_____ c. During Wednesday night prayer meeting, a person tells of her burden to reach out to the massive new housing developments on the north side of town. A young adult speaks up and says he lives in that area and has had a burden to reach out to his neighbors. A Sunday school teacher tells how her class was praying about that very need on Sunday and sensed that your church needs to do something. After a time of prayer, you sense God's leadership to volunteer for a task force to seek ways to reach this new community for Christ.

_____ d. During your prayer time, you intercede for missions work being done in other countries. You remember that a missions speaker from the Ukraine told about the need for medical supplies for the people in the city of Lugansk. As you're praying for this need, you remember hearing that a medical clinic in town has gone out of business. You tell your church of the need, and they decide to purchase the clinic's equipment and ship it to your missionary contact in Lugansk.

In the illustrations above, we matched the case studies and ways of God this way: a-3, b-1, c-4, and d-2. Ministry to the beggar began with a circumstance. Conviction about right relationships at work began with the Scriptures. Your involvement in the church's decision to seek to reach the new housing development began as you heard other believers speak. The connection between the need for medical supplies and the opportunity to buy the clinic's equipment began as you were praying. God is very creative, and He can reveal an assignment to you in any number of ways. Always be open to His leading throughout your day.

➤16. Think about the spiritual needs in the lives of people around you. Have you sensed a particular burden for one or more of these people or groups? In the list below, check the "people group" or groups that God seems to have given you a special concern for as you pray.

❑ spouse          ❑ neighbors          ❑ needy group in your city

❑ parents         ❑ coworkers          ❑ needy group in your state

❑ children        ❑ church members     ❑ needy group in your nation

❑ relatives       ❑ students           ❑ needy group in another country

➤17. Use the lines in the margin to write names of individuals or groups for which you have sensed a God-given burden to minister to their needs—even if you don't know yet what He would have you do.

➤18. Read the words of the following song. Let God speak to you through them. If a statement or phrase is particularly meaningful to you, underline it.

**Hark, the Voice of Jesus Calling**
by Daniel March

Hark, the voice of Jesus calling—"Who will go and work today?
Fields are white and harvests waiting, Who will bear the sheaves away?"
Loud and long the Master calleth, Rich reward He offers free;
Who will answer, gladly saying, "Here am I; send me, send me"?

If you cannot cross the ocean And the heathen lands explore,
You can find the heathen nearer, You can help them at your door;
If you cannot give your thousands, You can give the widow's mite;
And the least you give for Jesus Will be precious in His sight.

Let none hear you idly saying, "There is nothing I can do,"
While the souls of men are dying And the Master calls for you.
Take the task He gives you gladly; Let His work your pleasure be;
Answer quickly when He calleth, "Here am I; send me, send me."

 19. Talk to the Lord about His desires for your servanthood. As you sense He may be speaking to you, write notes in the margin. Ask Him,

- Where and how would You like me to serve You?
- What preparations do You want to make in my life to prepare me?
- What character traits of a servant do You want to develop in my life that are not there yet?
- What adjustments must I make to be free to follow You?
- What are ways You have ministered to me that have prepared me for ministry to others?
- Who are the individuals around my life that You would have me serve as if they were You?

 Close by surrendering your life to be available to the Lord as His servant in whatever way He might want to use you. Pray like Isaiah, "Here am I, send me." If you're not yet ready to make that surrender, at least give Him permission to help you want to be willing.

# MINICHURCH MEETING 10

## BEFORE THE MEETING

❏ 1. Turn to "Preparing for Your Minichurch Meeting" on page 143. Use it as a guide to get ready for this meeting. Check the box above after you have prepared.

❏ 2. Unless God should direct otherwise, your minichurch leader will be using the following outline to guide your meeting. You may want to look over the questions and activities so you will be better prepared to participate.

## DURING THE MEETING

❖ **Opening Prayer**

❖ **Singing Together**

Consider singing "Hark, the Voice of Jesus Calling," "Make Me a Blessing," or "Ready" together with other choruses and hymns.

❖ **Building Relationships**

1. What's a way a person acted as a servant to you that was especially meaningful or helpful?
2. How have you been humbled and deeply moved by the servant ministry of a brother or sister in Christ?

❖ **Praying for One Another** (in fours or sixes)

Based on the study this week, how can we pray for you to be a more effective servant of God? Take time to pray specifically for each person's request.

❖ **Interacting with the Scriptures** (in fours or sixes)

1. What verse or passage of Scripture has been most meaningful or challenging to you this week? How has God used it to speak to you? What significant actions have you taken this week because of something God revealed through His Word?
2. (p. 106) Volunteers: Recite the memory verse you have learned this week, and explain any special meaning you've gained from it.
3. (p. 106, #5) What word or phrase from Ephesians 3:1-9 and 13 have you come to better understand or experience this week? Describe your understanding or experience.

❖ **Reviewing the Lesson**

1. (p. 108, #7) What do we know about Paul's calling to be a servant of God to the Gentiles? Take turns stating details about his early life and calling. As time permits, you may want to look at one or more of the other records of his calling: Acts 9:1-30; Acts 22:3-21; Galatians 1:11-24; and Galatians 2:1-10.
2. (p. 108) How was God's grace involved in Paul's calling and assignment?
3. (pp. 109-110, #9) From memory, see how many prin-

ciples of servanthood you can recall.
4. (p. 111) What are four ways God may reveal an assignment to you as a servant?

❖ **Applying the Truths to Life**

1. Why does obedience to God sometimes bring about suffering? Is suffering worth enduring? Why?
2. (pp. 109-110) Which of the principles of servanthood are the most difficult to practice? Why?
3. (p. 110, #10) Which principle do you need to improve on as you follow the Lord? Why?
4. What are some ways God has called you to be His servant in a specific circumstance or in a longer-term ministry?
5. How have you personally experienced God revealing assignments to you?
6. (p. 112) How effectively has your church (or minichurch) been able to understand the ways God is calling your church to assignments? What are some ways you can improve on listening to God together?
7. (pp. 112-113, #16 and #17) What are some of the special concerns or burdens God has given you? Are some of the burdens common to two or more people in your minichurch?
8. What assignments, if any, do you sense God may be trying to call you to?
9. Volunteers: (p. 113, #19) What do you sense God is saying to you about your servanthood?

❖ **Responding to God in Prayer**

Pray about the burdens, concerns, and/or assignments you sense God has given you as individuals and as a minichurch. Ask Him what you need to do in response to Him. Ask Him to give you a clear sense of calling to those assignments that are from Him. Ask Him to reveal His timing for those assignments as well.

❖ **Ministering to One Another**

What needs (if any) of members have you become aware of during this meeting that the Body needs to care for? What can we do to meet the needs or to help connect the person with those who can help? Are there things we need to do now or this week to help?

❖ **Reaching Out to Others**

Are there persons in your circles of influence who need a saving relationship with Jesus Christ for whom God seems to be giving you a special burden? Are any of these the ones you sense are God's assignment to you? What can we pray or do to help you carry this burden or to fulfill this assignment?

❖ **Closing Prayer**

❖ **Optional: "Breaking Bread" Together**

# LESSON 11
# REVEALING GOD'S GLORY

**Racial Healing and God's Glory**

In the spring of 1992, South Central Los Angeles exploded with rioting, looting, assault, and arson. The city was in flames as Americans watched their news broadcasts. The acquittal of the policemen who had beaten Rodney King provided a sufficient reason for people to vent their racial hatred toward others. With all that has been done in this country to remove the problems of racism over the past few decades, we saw clear evidence that racism was still alive and well. Across the nation, cities braced for potential outbreaks of rioting where racial tensions were high.

In August of that year, I (Claude) received a call from a pastor in Austin, Texas. He said that the leaders in Austin were afraid they might experience race riots because of the tensions in their community. A group of pastors had been meeting and praying about the problem. They decided to hold a sacred (or solemn) assembly of pastors from the white, black, and Hispanic communities to seek the Lord on behalf of their city. They asked if I would come to help.

For two days, a group of 30 or 40 pastors met for a time of fasting, prayer, confession of sin, and seeking the Lord. We examined the Scriptures to see that when an emergency arises that's due to sin, a sacred assembly is God's way for His people to seek Him and return to Him (Joel 1:14; 2:12-15). They described how highways that divided their city north, south, east, and west were symbolic of the racial and class divisions of their city. I became an observer as I watched these men begin to deal seriously with their own sins of racism. They also identified the sins of those who had gone before them to see if those sins continued to be evident.

**Joel 1:14**

"Declare a holy fast; call a sacred assembly. Summon the elders and all who live in the land to the house of the LORD your God, and cry out to the LORD."

**Joel 2:12-15**

"'Even now,' declares the LORD, 'return to me with all your heart, with fasting and weeping and mourning.' Rend your heart and not your garments. Return to the LORD your God, for he is gracious and compassionate, slow to anger and abounding in love, and he relents from sending calamity. Who knows? He may turn and have pity and leave behind a blessing . . . . Blow the trumpet in Zion, declare a holy fast, call a sacred assembly."

I remember one black pastor stating a burden he had for the broken families and irresponsible fathers in his church community. As we were praying for him and his church, a white pastor recalled how his forefathers had split up black families when a husband and wife were sold separately on the slave block to the highest bidders. Following the pattern in Nehemiah 9 and Daniel 9, he asked the Lord's forgiveness for the sins of his forefathers that had contributed to the breakdown of the black family. Then he began to pray for healing of the families. He prayed for this pastor to receive wisdom to help his families be restored and for fathers to learn a new commitment to family life.

We turned to the oldest black pastor present and asked him to tell us what it was like for him growing up. He described several demeaning and humiliating experiences. Then he said, "My dream as a teenager was to walk into downtown with a machine gun and kill as many white people as possible before they killed me." He then began to weep as he said, "But when I came to Christ, all that changed." A white pastor moved to his side and placed his arm around his shoulder and began to pray. He asked for forgiveness for ways he had neglected to take a stand for the oppressed. He began to weep for his fellow pastor. He thanked God for the change Christ had made in his life, and he asked the Lord to heal all the remaining brokenness in his life so that he might be brought to wholeness and complete health.

After two days of similar experiences, we gathered all the Hispanic pastors in the center of the room, laid hands on them, and prayed for God's blessing on their ministries. We did the same for the black pastors and the white pastors. I saw the cords

115

of love draw these pastors together like probably none of us had experienced before. They were hugging and praying for each other. They were identifying with the woundedness and needs of their fellow pastors. They talked of ways their churches might be able to help each other. They made plans to begin meeting together regularly for one another and for the sake of their city.

The great mystery God had revealed to Paul and the apostles was that God, through the cross, made it possible for those who are very different (Jews and Gentiles) to become equal sharers in the promise of salvation. God's "intent was that now, through the church, the manifold wisdom of God should be made known to the rulers and authorities in the heavenly realms, according to his eternal purpose which he accomplished in Christ Jesus our Lord. In him and through faith in him we may approach God with freedom and confidence" (Eph. 3:10-12). This week, we want to see how God's desire is to get glory through the church as it reveals His wisdom and power. I've seen a glimmer of that wisdom and power in Austin, Texas. We pray you'll experience it and reveal God's glory where you are.

 Pause to pray. Is the Body of Christ where you attend a clear picture of the unity that Christ has provided? Is the larger Body of Christ in your city or community healthy, strong, and united in the love of Christ and for one another? Ask God to speak to you this week about the ways He would like to work through His Body to reveal His glory.

## PART 1: INTERACTING WITH THE SCRIPTURES

### Reading / Hearing God's Word

➤1. Select one of the reading (or listening) options in the margin. Using your Bible, read or listen to the passage of Scripture. As you begin, ask God to speak to you through His Word. Watch for one verse or idea that's especially meaningful to you. Once you finish reading, check the box indicating the passage you read.

### Meditating on God's Word

➤2. In the margin, write a brief summary of the meaningful verse or idea you just identified.

### Memorizing God's Word

➤3. Select and tear out a new Scripture memory card from the back of your book, or continue reviewing one you started learning earlier. For a new verse, use the tips for memorizing Scripture on your bookmark.

### Understanding God's Word

➤4. Read again the focal passage for this week's lesson (Eph. 3:10-12, 20-21) in the margin. Underline any key phrases or ideas that seem especially meaningful to you. Then read the brief definitions of key words below to prepare yourself for the remainder of the lesson.

♦ **intent:** plan, desire.

♦ **church:** the whole community of Christians, all saints both in heaven and on earth.

♦ **manifold:** with much variety, multifaceted.

♦ **wisdom:** understanding of the true nature of things.

♦ **rulers:** those chief in rank, magistrates, leaders.

♦ **authorities:** ones with delegated influence, jurisdiction.

♦ **heavenly realms:** the heavenlies, celestial.

---

**Read or Listen to:**

❑ Ephesians 1–6

❑ Ephesians 1–3

❑ Ephesians 3:1-21

**Meaningful Verse or Idea**

_____

_____

**Ephesians 3:10-12, 20-21**

"His intent was that now, through the church, the manifold wisdom of God should be made known to the rulers and authorities in the heavenly realms, according to his eternal purpose which he accomplished in Christ Jesus our Lord. In him and through faith in him we may approach God with freedom and confidence....

"Now to him who is able to do immeasurably more than all we ask or imagine, according to his power that is at work within us, to him be glory in the church and in Christ Jesus throughout all generations, for ever and ever! Amen."

♦ **eternal:** for evermore, without end, continued duration.

♦ **purpose:** intention, proposal, a setting forth.

♦ **faith:** reliance upon Christ for salvation, trust, loyalty to Christ, continuing to trust in Christ, fidelity.

♦ **freedom:** access, admission.

♦ **confidence:** reliance, trust.

♦ **immeasurably more:** exceeding abundantly, superior to.

♦ **glory:** splendor, dignified, honorable, praiseworthy; evidence of God's wonderful work or character, honor.

♦ **generations:** ages of time or people.

➤5. Look back through this list of words. Circle one that you would like to understand or experience more fully.

**Looking through the Scripture to God**

 Now pause to pray.

- Ask the Lord to help you understand what Paul wrote about the mystery of Christ as you study this week.
- Ask God to help you grasp the magnitude of His great riches that He has made available through Christ.
- Ask the Lord to help your church and the larger Body of Christ to become all that He intends so that His manifold wisdom may be revealed.
- Thank the Lord that you can come to Him with freedom and confidence with your prayers.
- Ask God to get glory through you and your church.
- Close by praying Ephesians 1:17-19 and 3:16-19 (on your bookmark) for yourself and your minichurch.

## PART 2: THE MYSTERY REVEALED AND REVEALING

In last week's lesson, we focused on Paul's calling to be God's servant. In that Scripture passage, Paul talked about the mystery God had revealed to him.

➤6. Review Ephesians 3:2-6 in the left margin. Circle *mystery* each time it occurs.

➤7. Based on Ephesians 3:6, what three relationships do the Gentiles now have with other believers, including those who are Jews? Fill in the blanks.

"This mystery is that through the gospel the Gentiles are

_____ together with Israel,

_____ together of one body, and

_____ together in the promise in Christ Jesus."

➤8. Paul mentioned this mystery in several other passages. Read the three scriptures about the mystery below. Circle the word *mystery* each time it occurs.

**Romans 16:25-27**—"Now to him who is able to establish you by my gospel and the proclamation of Jesus Christ, according to the revelation of the mystery hidden for long ages past, but now revealed and made known through the prophetic writings by the command of the eternal God, so that all nations might believe and obey him—to the only wise God be glory forever through Jesus Christ! Amen."

**Ephesians 3:2-6**

"²Surely you have heard about the administration of God's grace that was given to me for you, ³that is, the mystery made known to me by revelation, as I have already written briefly. ⁴In reading this, then, you will be able to understand my insight into the mystery of Christ, ⁵which was not made known to men in other generations as it has now been revealed by the Spirit to God's holy apostles and prophets. ⁶This mystery is that through the gospel the Gentiles are heirs together with Israel, members together of one body, and sharers together in the promise in Christ Jesus."

**Ephesians 1:9-10**—"He made known to us the mystery of his will according to his good pleasure, which he purposed in Christ, to be put into effect when the times will have reached their fulfillment—to bring all things in heaven and on earth together under one head, even Christ."

**Colossians 1:27**—"To them God has chosen to make known among the Gentiles the glorious riches of this mystery, which is Christ in you, the hope of glory."

To be "heirs together" means that all men and women, whether Jews or Gentiles, can share in the same spiritual inheritance. Paul wrote to the Galatians, "There is neither Jew nor Greek, slave nor free, male nor female, for you are all one in Christ Jesus. If you belong to Christ, then you are Abraham's seed, and heirs according to the promise" (Gal. 3:28-29). God's promise to Abraham, hundreds of years before Christ came (Gen. 12:1-3), included not only the Jews but also the Gentiles. We are "heirs together" in God's eternal kingdom.

To be "members together of one body" is not only a "positional" truth, but also a reality that is practical and functional. Paul used a Greek word here to express this concept. As far as we know, this word was never used before in the Greek language. Some believe Paul coined the term to explain this marvelous mystery. Evidently he could find no word or words rich enough in meaning to describe the meaning of it all.

Not only are all people who put their faith in Christ "heirs together in God's eternal kingdom," but we are "members together" in the here and now. The "one body" of Jesus Christ is a present reality in the church. Every believer is a significant part of the Body of Christ, just as every member of our physical body is a significant part of the whole. We need one another to be complete.

To be "sharers together" involves both realities. We all share in our eternal inheritance, and we all share in one another's lives in the here and now. There will be no barriers in heaven, and there should be no barriers among Christians on earth. A part of the good news to the Gentile Christians was that they were equal before God with all other believers. They didn't have to be second-class members! Thus, Paul wrote earlier in the Ephesian letter,

> "He himself is our peace, who has made the two one and has destroyed the barrier, the dividing wall of hostility . . . . His purpose was to create in himself one new man out of the two, thus making peace, and in this one body to reconcile both of them to God through the cross, by which he put to death their hostility" (Eph. 2:14-16).

➤9. **Which of the following barriers or distinctions do you think were removed by Christ at the cross? Check all you think He removed.**

❑ racial barriers                           ❑ ethnic heritage barriers
❑ gender (male/female) barriers             ❑ age barriers
❑ class barriers                            ❑ financial barriers
❑ national origin barriers                  ❑ previous religious affiliation

Did you check them all? You could have. Jesus removed every barrier or distinction between believers. We're all first-class members of His Body, and we're fellow heirs of His eternal inheritance. Praise the Lord!

This marvelous mystery regarding the hope of eternal life for all who believe in Jesus Christ was unveiled to Paul in a special way. He received his "insight into the mystery of Christ" (Eph. 3:4) by special revelation. This means that God spoke to him directly. This process began on the Damascus road, resulting in his conversion to Jesus Christ (Acts 9:3-6). The process continued for the next several years.

Through Paul's ministry to the Gentiles, God made this mystery a reality in the church. Then God revealed more of His eternal purpose:

> "His intent was that now, through the church, the manifold wisdom of God should be made known to the rulers and authorities in the heavenly realms, according to his eternal purpose which he accomplished in Christ Jesus our Lord" (Eph. 3:10-11).

▶10. **Based on this scripture, answer these questions:**

1. When did God intend to reveal His wisdom? _____

2. Through whom would God reveal His wisdom? _____

3. To whom did God intend to make known His manifold wisdom?

_____

4. When did God make these plans that were accomplished in Christ?
❏ a. recently, on the spur of the moment    ❏ b. in eternity past

God had planned from eternity past (4b) to reveal this wonderful mystery of redemption through Christ. He revealed the mystery to Paul and the apostles and prophets because "now" was the time He wanted to reveal His wisdom to "rulers and authorities in the heavenly realms." God's great master plan was to reveal His "manifold wisdom" "through the church."

Who were these "rulers and authorities" that God had in mind? Paul used these two terms to refer to human rulers in Titus 3:1: "Remind the people to be subject to rulers and authorities, to be obedient, to be ready to do whatever is good"; and in Romans 13:1: "Everyone must submit himself to the governing authorities." But in this week's text he described these "rulers and authorities" as being in "the heavenly realms." They can't be earthly human rulers.

Many commentators automatically assume that the terms refer to the angels in heaven. Peter, in describing salvation, said, "Even angels long to look into these things" (1 Pet. 1:12). Before we settle on that conclusion, however, let's look at how Paul used these terms in referring to beings in other texts.

▶11. **Read the scriptures in the margin. Then check below whom you think Paul may have been referring to by the terms "rulers and authorities."**
❏ a. God's faithful angels    ❏ b. demonic powers in the heavenlies

Why would God care to show Satan and his demons His "manifold (multifaceted or varigated) wisdom"? God chooses to reveal Himself and His glory to all of His creation. We'll look at this subject in more detail in the next part of our lesson. For now, let's look at the experience of a man named Job.

> "One day the angels came to present themselves before the LORD, and Satan also came with them. The LORD said to Satan, 'Where have you come from?'
>
> "Satan answered the LORD, 'From roaming through the earth and going back and forth in it.'
>
> "Then the LORD said to Satan, 'Have you considered my servant Job? There is no one on earth like him; he is blameless and upright, a man who fears God and shuns evil'" (Job 1:6-8).

A meeting took place in heaven, and Satan attended along with the angels. God pointed to His servant Job as a wonderful example of a godly man. Satan claimed that Job only feared God because of all the good God did for him. So God gave Satan per-

## RULERS AND AUTHORITIES

### Colossians 2:10, 15

"You have been given fullness in Christ, who is the head over every power and authority. . . . And having disarmed the powers [rulers] and authorities, he made a public spectacle of them, triumphing over them by the cross."

### 1 Corinthians 15:24

"Then the end will come, when he hands over the kingdom to God the Father after he has destroyed all dominion [rule], authority and power."

### Ephesians 1:21

"Far above all rule and authority, power and dominion, and every title that can be given, not only in the present age but also in the one to come."

### Ephesians 2:2

"In which you used to live when you followed the ways of this world and of the ruler of the kingdom of the air, the spirit who is now at work in those who are disobedient."

### Ephesians 6:12

"Our struggle is not against flesh and blood, but against the rulers, against the authorities, against the powers of this dark world and against the spiritual forces of evil in the heavenly realms."

mission to take everything away Job had, including his children. Then another meeting took place in heaven:

> "Then the LORD said to Satan, 'Have you considered my servant Job? There is no one on earth like him; he is blameless and upright, a man who fears God and shuns evil. And he still maintains his integrity, though you incited me against him to ruin him without any reason'" (Job 2:3).

Job came through the test, and God was proud of him. Job revealed God's glory. The test continued when God gave Satan permission to take away Job's health. In the end, God restored Job, and "the LORD blessed the latter part of Job's life more than the first. . . . And so he died, old and full of years" (Job 42:12, 17).

Evidently, at one time meetings took place in heaven that Satan and his followers attended. God's intent is to reveal to these "rulers and authorities" His greatness, power, and wisdom. The world can't do anything to solve the problems of human conflict, but in the church of Jesus Christ, God can bring people of great diversity together in a beautiful display of unity. This proves God's greatness and the wisdom of His plan of redemption through the cross. The unity of the church becomes a reminder to satanic forces that they are defeated foes.

➤ 12. If a heavenly meeting took place between Satan and God, could God point to your life, family, or church as an example of what His wisdom, power, and grace can do to produce godliness and holiness in a redeemed person or a redeemed people? What do you think God would say about you?

_____

_____

 Talk to the Lord about your response to the last question. Thank Him for all He has done in you and for you. Ask Him to continue His work until it is perfected in your life in a way that would bring Him glory.

## PART 3: GOD'S GLORY IN THE CHURCH

In the final lesson of our study, we're going to focus in more detail on Paul's prayer for the saints that you've been praying for your minichurch throughout the course. At the conclusion of his prayer, Paul gave a great closing statement of praise:

> "Now to him who is able to do immeasurably more than all we ask or imagine, according to his power that is at work within us, to him be glory in the church and in Christ Jesus throughout all generations, for ever and ever! Amen" (Eph. 3:20-21).

Someone has said, "Beware of superlatives. Usually they are used to stretch the truth." However, there's no exaggeration in Paul's concluding statements in his grand doxology. God "is able to do immeasurably more than all we ask or imagine." The reason is related "to his power that is at work within us" (Eph. 3:20).

In Ephesians 1, Paul spoke of God's incomparable power (v. 19). There's nothing to compare with His omnipotence (all-power). In chapter 3, he spoke of God's unsearchable riches (v. 8). That also is true. It's no exaggerated comment, no hyperbolic statement to make a point. God's grace and all that it means are unsearchable, far beyond our understanding. As he concluded this opening section of the letter describing God's power in saving us, keeping us, and encouraging us, Paul described the Lord's resources as immeasurable.

## God's Glory

**Revelation 4:11**—"You are worthy, our Lord and God, to receive glory and honor and power, for you created all things, and by your will they were created and have their being."

**Psalm 29:1-2**—"Ascribe to the LORD, O mighty ones, ascribe to the LORD glory and strength. Ascribe to the LORD the glory due his name; worship the LORD in the splendor of his holiness."

**Psalm 96:3-4, 7-10**—"Declare his glory among the nations, his marvelous deeds among all peoples. For great is the LORD and most worthy of praise; he is to be feared above all gods. . . . Ascribe to the LORD, O families of nations, ascribe to the LORD glory and strength. Ascribe to the LORD the glory due his name; bring an offering and come into his courts. Worship the LORD in the splendor of his holiness; tremble before him, all the earth. Say among the nations, 'The LORD reigns.'"

**Psalm 115:1**—"Not to us, O LORD, not to us but to your name be the glory, because of your love and faithfulness."

**Isaiah 26:8**—"Yes, LORD, . . . your name and renown are the desire of our hearts."

**Isaiah 42:8**—"I am the LORD; that is my name! I will not give my glory to another or my praise to idols."

**Isaiah 26:15**—"O LORD; you have enlarged the nation. You have gained glory for yourself; you have extended all the borders of the land."

So much about God is far beyond our understanding. No wonder Paul said, "To him be glory in the church and in Christ Jesus throughout all generations, for ever and ever! Amen" (Eph. 3:21). He is deserving of all glory and praise.

▶ **13. Read the scriptures in the margin to see what they have to say about God's glory. Circle the word *glory* each time it appears.**

 **Spend a few minutes to give glory and praise to God in prayer. Ask Him to reveal to you ways the church can reveal His glory and please Him.**

Notice that Paul prayed in his doxology that God will receive glory "in the church and in Christ Jesus." Just as God received glory though the godly life of Job, so He desires to reveal His glory through the church—the living Body of His Son, Jesus Christ. Just as God revealed His glory through Jesus during His earthly life, so God wants to reveal His glory through the Body of Christ in our generation—and in every generation.

▶ **14. Read the following verses from John's gospel that tell about Jesus and His glory. Again, circle the word *glory* each time it appears.**

John 2:11—"This, the first of his miraculous signs, Jesus performed in Cana in Galilee. He thus revealed his glory, and his disciples put their faith in him."

John 8:54—"Jesus replied, 'If I glorify myself, my glory means nothing. My Father, whom you claim as your God, is the one who glorifies me.'"

John 11:4—"When he heard this, Jesus said, 'This sickness will not end in death. No, it is for God's glory so that God's Son may be glorified through it.'"

God the Father brought glory to His Son, Jesus. When Jesus' glory was revealed at Cana, the disciples placed their faith in Him. When Jesus raised Lazarus from the dead, God glorified His Son. When God reveals His greatness that cannot be matched by the world, He receives glory.

When the mystery of God's grace becomes a reality in the life and practice of the church, God receives glory. The world can't take groups that are hostile to one another and cause them to love one another and live in harmony, unity, and oneness. But God can. His desire is for His people to live out the reality of this great mystery so that He will get glory. He planned in advance for us to reveal His glory. "What if he did this to make the riches of his glory known to the objects of his mercy, whom he prepared in advance for glory—even us, whom he also called, not only from the Jews but also from the Gentiles?" (Rom. 9:23-24). "We, who with unveiled faces all reflect the Lord's glory, are being transformed into his likeness with ever-increasing glory, which comes from the Lord, who is the Spirit" (2 Cor. 3:18).

▶ **15. Which of the following two illustrations seems to more nearly reflect the kind of glory God would want from His people? Check one.**

❑ a. The Christians in community X are all proud people. They have a tendency to be critical and judgmental of other churches and Christians. They see themselves in competition with one another. They seldom cooperate on any project for fear that someone else might get the credit or that their members will be corrupted by the influence of others. Local government leaders and workers accused of racist actions are active members of local Christian congregations. They see no inconsistency in their actions at work and their faith in Christ.

❑ b. The Christians in Modesto, California, have come to see themselves as members of the church of Modesto under their head, Jesus Christ. Local congregations see themselves as "churches within the church of Modesto." Every

Wednesday, more than 100 pastors from every Christian denomination meet to pray for each other and for their city. By working together in their wedding policies, the pastors have seen a 27 percent drop in the divorce rate in the city. Churches from different racial and ethnic backgrounds get together regularly for worship and celebration of their common Lord. They seek to help meet needs of sister churches. They have united in enlisting lighthouses of prayer to see that every home in Modesto is prayed for regularly and receives an opportunity to respond to the gospel of Jesus Christ. Their passion is to see their city come to Christ.

The Christians in Modesto, California, are revealing God's glory to a watching world. They are revealing God's great wisdom to "rulers and authorities in heavenly realms." These believers haven't fully arrived, but they certainly are moving in the right direction.

**Turn to the Lord in prayer. Talk to Him about His glory that is revealed in your life, your family, your minichurch, your church, and your city. If His glory is not as evident as it should be, ask Him to begin pointing out the areas that need to change so you will more nearly reflect His likeness in all you do. Read through or sing "To God Be the Glory" in the margin as you close your study time for Part 3.**

## PART 4: GOD'S GLORY AND YOU

When God has worked in your life in such a way that His glory is being reflected, you will begin to feel like Paul—as the least of the least of God's saints. We are all so unworthy and undeserving. Everything of God's glory in us is pure grace. Any glory revealed through your life is only because He has done a good work in you. It is His glory, after all. You should respond to God's great work in you with humility.

Some Christians become confused at this point. They interpret humility and meekness as weakness. To them, humility is being withdrawn and inactive or overly critical of yourself. Not at all! In fact, many of our personality traits will remain the same but are now devoted to doing God's will, not our own. Thus it was with Paul. He had a strong personality and zeal for the Lord, but he knew his relationship with the Lord was purely because of His mercy and grace.

▶**16. Read the two Scripture passages in the margin that speak of humility. Which of the following attitudes do you want to be true of your life? Check one.**

❑ a. I want to be proud, arrogant, and lofty so I can look down on others.
❑ b. I want to be humble like Christ and live as a servant to others.

As you seek to reveal God's glory in the days to come, here are a few ideas that may help you get in line with what God wants to do through you.

▶**17. As you read this list, circle the numbers of any that you think will be most helpful. Look up and read the scriptures also.**

1. The more you die to self and sin, the more the glory of the indwelling Christ shows in your life (Gal. 2:20).
2. When you are reconciled with God through the cross, He works to establish a close, loving fellowship (*koinonia*) between you and other believers (1 John 1:3, 7).
3. Following God's leadership, you should remove any human barriers that separate you from the rest of the Body of Christ. See all other believers as fellow members of His Body.
4. You should follow God's model in relationships with other believers by accept-

---

**To God Be the Glory**
by Fanny J. Crosby

To God be the glory,
great things He hath done;
So loved He the world
that He gave us His Son,
Who yielded His life
an atonement for sin,
And opened the life-gate
that all may go in.

Praise the Lord,
praise the Lord,
Let the earth hear His voice!
Praise the Lord,
praise the Lord,
Let the people rejoice!
O come to the Father,
thro' Jesus the Son,
And give Him the glory,
great things He hath done.

**Philippians 2:5-8**—"Your attitude should be the same as that of Christ Jesus: Who, being in very nature God, did not consider equality with God something to be grasped, but made himself nothing, taking the very nature of a servant, being made in human likeness. And being found in appearance as a man, he humbled himself and became obedient to death — even death on a cross!"

**1 Peter 5:5-6**—"All of you, clothe yourselves with humility toward one another, because, 'God opposes the proud but gives grace to the humble.' Humble yourselves, therefore, under God's mighty hand, that he may lift you up in due time."

ing (Rom. 15:7), forgiving (Col. 3:13), loving (John 13:34), serving (Matt. 20:25-28), and comforting (2 Cor. 1:3-4), just as He has done for you.

5. Demonstrate love like the Good Samaritan's (Luke 10:25-37) toward other members of the Body of Christ (individuals or churches). If you see any need or a place where health is lacking, turn to the Lord and ask, "Father, how can You work through me to show love to my brother?" Then do all He guides and provides for you to do.

 **18. Conclude this lesson in prayer. Ask the Lord to evaluate your life, family, minichurch, church, and even citywide church. Write some notes to yourself in the margin or on separate paper.**

- How is He revealing His glory through you?
- What, if anything, is in the way of His revealing more of His glory?
- How would the Lord like to reveal His manifold wisdom through you in relationship to others who are racially or ethnically different?
- What does the Lord want to do to improve the reality of unity in the Body of Christ where you are (your congregation and your city)?

# MINICHURCH MEETING 11

## BEFORE THE MEETING

❑ 1. Turn to "Preparing for Your Minichurch Meeting" on page 143. Use it as a guide to get ready for this meeting. Check the box above after you have prepared.

❑ 2. Unless God should direct otherwise, your minichurch leader will be using the following outline to guide your meeting. You may want to look over the questions and activities so you will be better prepared to participate.

## DURING THE MEETING

### ❖ Opening Prayer

### ❖ Singing Together

Consider singing "In Christ There Is No East or West," "To God Be the Glory," or "Bless Be the Tie That Binds" together with other choruses and hymns.

### ❖ Building Relationships

1. Instead of talking about yourself this week, respond to this question: What have you observed in the lives of minichurch members during the past 11 weeks that reflects godliness, spiritual fruit, or God's glory? Be specific in naming an individual and what you have seen.

### ❖ Responding to God in Prayer

Volunteers: Lead the group in praising God. Ascribe glory, honor, and praise to Him.

### ❖ Interacting with the Scriptures (in fours or sixes)

1. What verse or passage of Scripture has been most meaningful or challenging to you this week? How has God used it to speak to you? What significant actions have you taken this week because of something God revealed through His Word?

2. (p. 116) Volunteers: Recite the memory verse you have learned this week, and explain any special meaning you have gained from it.

3. (p. 117, #5) What word or phrase from Ephesians 3:10-12 and 20-21 have you come to better understand or experience this week? Describe your understanding or experience.

### ❖ Reviewing the Lesson

1. (pp. 117-118) What mystery did God reveal to Paul?

2. (p. 119, #11) Who are the "rulers and authorities" to whom God wants to reveal His wisdom? Why do you think God would want to reveal the wisdom of His plan for redemption to Satan and the demonic rulers?

3. (p. 121, #13) What have you learned about God's glory?

4. (p. 121) How did God reveal His glory through Jesus? How did people respond?

### ❖ Applying the Truths to Life

1. (p. 118, #9) Which of the barriers that Christ removed at the cross still seem to keep Christians in your church or community separated from each other? What do you sense God would want to do about removing those barriers?

2. (p. 120, #12) What kind of model of God's wisdom would your church prove to be? How do you think God would describe your church to Satan?

3. Think about the Christians and churches you know. Who are the individuals and churches that seem to reveal more of God's glory? After mentioning these, pause to thank God for what He has revealed through them.

4. (p. 121) How does God reveal His glory in a church? in a community?

5. (pp. 121-122, #15) Which of the two illustrations is more like your community? Is there a spirit of unity and cooperation? Or is there division, competition, and criticism?

6. (p. 122) Who are some Christians you have known or observed who seem to have a genuine spirit of humility? What did it look like?

7. (pp. 122-123, #17) Which of the suggestions do you sense might be most helpful in revealing more of God's glory through you? your church?

8. (p. 123, #18) What do you sense God wants you to do to reveal more of His glory? How has He been speaking to you this week?

### ❖ Praying for One Another (in fours or sixes)

As you have just responded to the questions above, you probably have identified a number of ways you need prayer. What one or two things do you most want your minichurch members to pray for you? As a member states a request, pray for him or her before moving to the next person.

### ❖ Ministering to Others in the Body

Has God revealed a lack of health or a need in another believer or another church that you sense He wants you or your church to help meet? Discuss.

### ❖ Reaching Out to Others

Who are the persons who need a saving relationship with Jesus Christ for whom God seems to be giving you a special burden? What can we pray or do to help you carry this burden?

### ❖ Closing Prayer

Gather in a circle, and take time to pray for your congregation. Pray that God will reveal His glory through your church.

### ❖ Optional: "Breaking Bread" Together

# LESSON 12
# PRAYING FOR THE SAINTS

**Our Riches in Christ**

Paul began his letter to the Ephesians describing the spiritual blessings God has lavished on us. He ended his prayer in chapter 3 by saying God is "able to do immeasurably more than all we ask or imagine, according to his power that is at work within us" (Eph. 3:20). Truly, as believers in Jesus Christ, we have been blessed with every spiritual blessing in Christ. These blessings go far beyond what we can even understand or describe with words. We are deeply blessed, and we're spiritually rich. Someone has attempted to summarize our riches in Christ this way:

In Christ we have:

- A love that can never be fathomed
- A life that can never die
- A righteousness that can never be tarnished
- A peace that can never be understood
- A rest that can never be disturbed
- A joy that can never be diminished
- A hope that can never be disappointed
- A glory that can never be clouded
- A light that can never be darkened
- A happiness that can never be interrupted
- A strength that can never be enfeebled
- A purity that can never be defiled
- A beauty that can never be marred
- A wisdom that can never be baffled
- Resources that can never be exhausted.

In many respects, this is what Paul was communicating to the followers of Jesus Christ in his Ephesian letter. Some of these things are guaranteed by virtue of our personal relationship with Christ, such as God's unconditional love, a hope that will never fade, and a righteousness that goes on forever. Many of these things, however, are potentially ours if we choose to grow and mature in our relationship with God and take advantage of the divine resources available to us. In the final part of his prayer for the saints, Paul prayed that they would, indeed, continue to grow into full maturity in Christ.

## PART 1: INTERACTING WITH THE SCRIPTURES

### Reading / Hearing God's Word

➤1. Select one of the reading (or listening) options in the margin. Using your Bible, read or listen to the passage of Scripture. As you begin, ask God to speak to you through His Word. Watch for one verse or idea that's especially meaningful to you. Once you finish reading, check the box indicating the passage you read.

### Meditating on God's Word

➤2. In the margin, write a brief summary of the meaningful verse or idea you just identified.

**Read or Listen to:**

❑ Ephesians 1–6
❑ Ephesians 1–3
❑ Ephesians 3:1-21

**Meaningful Verse or Idea**

_____

_____

Memorizing God's Word

➤3. Select and tear out a final Scripture memory card from the back of your book, or continue reviewing one you started learning earlier. For a new verse, use the tips for memorizing Scripture on your bookmark.

Understanding God's Word

➤4. Read again the focal passage for this week's lesson (Eph. 3:14-19) in the margin. Underline any key phrases or ideas that seem especially meaningful to you. Then read the brief definitions of key words below. This will prepare you for the remainder of this week's study.

- **family:** descendants from the same father, kindred.
- **riches:** wealth, abundance, valuable bestowment.
- **strengthen:** to empower, increase in vigor, to wax strong.
- **power:** miraculous force, might, strength, ability.
- **inner being:** (inner man) inside, inward part of a person.
- **hearts:** thoughts, feelings.
- **faith:** reliance upon Christ for salvation, trust.
- **rooted:** stabilized.
- **established:** grounded, settled, foundation laid, consolidated.
- **love:** [*agape*] godly affection, seeking the very best for another unconditionally.
- **saints:** sacred ones, ones set apart as holy, set apart for God.
- **grasp:** comprehend, perceive, seize possession of.
- **surpasses:** beyond the usual mark, excel, pass, exceeding.
- **knowledge:** factual information, learning.

➤5. Look back through this list of words. Circle one that you would like to understand or experience more fully.

Looking through the Scripture to God

 Now pause to pray. You've been using this prayer throughout this course to pray for yourself and your minichurch. Take time to pray one more time through this prayer. Using your bookmark, reflect on each phrase and talk to the Lord.

- Thank God for the ways He already has answered this prayer during the past 12 weeks.
- Ask God to get glory through your church by doing far beyond all that you and your group can even think to pray.
- Close with Paul's doxology (prayer of praise) in the margin.

## PART 2: KNEELING BEFORE THE FATHER

Throughout our study of Ephesians 1–3, you've been praying Paul's prayer for yourself and your minichurch. Perhaps by now you have even memorized it. In many respects, it's a model for Christians to pray for others and for themselves. This prayer is appropriate for individual and corporate (group) prayer.

**Prayer Part I.** What appears to be two prayers in this letter is actually one. In fact, this single prayer in many respects forms the framework upon which Paul built his thoughts and ideas, beginning in verse 15 of chapter 1. Each time he began to pray, he said, "For this reason."

---

**Ephesians 3:14-19**

"For this reason I kneel before the Father, from whom his whole family in heaven and on earth derives its name. I pray that out of his glorious riches he may strengthen you with power through his Spirit in your inner being, so that Christ may dwell in your hearts through faith. And I pray that you, being rooted and established in love, may have power, together with all the saints, to grasp how wide and long and high and deep is the love of Christ, and to know this love that surpasses knowledge—that you may be filled to the measure of all the fullness of God."

**Paul's Doxology**

"Now to him who is able to do immeasurably more than all we ask or imagine, according to his power that is at work within us, to him be glory in the church and in Christ Jesus throughout all generations, for ever and ever! Amen" (Eph. 3:20-21).

The first time he used the phrase (Eph. 1:15), he had just stated why he was going to pray for these believers. They had been "included in Christ" when they "heard the word of truth" (Eph. 1:13), became Christians, and received the Holy Spirit. Because this was true, Paul asked God to help them grow and mature in their Christian lives. For each request in his prayer, Paul would then explain why he made the request. Here is a summary of his first two requests and his reasons.

**Request 1:** "I keep asking that the God of our Lord Jesus Christ, the glorious Father, may give you the Spirit of wisdom and revelation

**Reason 1:** "so that you may know him better."

**Request 2:** "I pray also that the eyes of your heart may be enlightened

**Reason 2:** "in order that you may know

- "the hope to which he has called you,
- "the riches of his glorious inheritance in the saints, and
- "his incomparably great power for us who believe."

➤6. **Match the request on the left with Paul's reason for making the request on the right. Write the number beside the letter.**

1. Spirit of wisdom and revelation        ____ a. know riches
2. Eyes of your heart be enlightened      ____ b. know God better
                                                   ____ c. know power
                                                   ____ d. know hope

As you have prayed these requests, have you seen any answers? To know if God were answering your prayers, you would look for the evidence (for the reasons). (Answers: 1-b; 2-a, c, d)

**ANSWERED PRAYER**

➤7. **How have you seen God answer these prayers for yourself and your minichurch? In other words, has anyone come to know God better? Has anyone come to experience the hope of his or her salvation? Has anyone come to know the riches of God's inheritance in the saints? Has anyone experienced God's power? What are some ways you have seen God answer? List some of the evidence in the margin.**

**Prayer Part II.** At the beginning in Ephesians 3, Paul decided to continue his prayer. To establish continuity in the reader's mind, he once again wrote, "For this reason" (Eph. 3:1). But he immediately decided to add a personal testimony (vv. 2-13) regarding his own calling to reveal the wonderful mystery "that through the gospel the Gentiles are heirs together with Israel, members together in one body, and sharers together in the promise in Christ Jesus" (Eph. 3:6). Because of what God has done for all of us, we have a wonderful foundation for prayer: "In him and through faith in him we may approach God with freedom and confidence" (Eph. 3:12).

In verse 14, Paul was ready to return to his prayer. He once again established continuity in the minds of the readers by saying, "For this reason." These believers were living proof that Gentiles can be saved. They, along with Paul and his fellow Jews, "were included in Christ" and had received the Holy Spirit (Eph. 1:13). Now Paul completed his prayer by making two additional requests. Building on what he had already asked God for on behalf of these believers, Paul prayed,

**Request 3:** "I pray that out of his glorious riches he may strengthen you with power through his Spirit in your inner being

**Reason 3:** "so that Christ may dwell in your hearts through faith."

**Request 4:** "I pray that you, being rooted and established in love, may have power, together with all the saints, to grasp how wide and long and high and deep is the love of Christ, and to know this love that surpasses knowledge—

**Reason 4:** "that you may be filled to the measure of all the fullness of God."

➤8. **Match the request on the left with Paul's reason for making the request on the right. Write the number beside the letter.**

1. Strengthen the inner man          ___ a. You may be filled to the fullness of God

2. Power to grasp the love of Christ  ___ b. Christ may dwell in your hearts through faith

As you have prayed these two requests, have you seen any answers to your prayers? Once again, to know if God were answering your prayers you would look for the evidence—the reasons you prayed the prayer to begin with. (Answers: 1-b; 2-a)

ANSWERED PRAYER

_____

_____

_____

_____

_____

_____

➤9. **How have you seen God answer these prayers for yourself and your minichurch? In other words, has anyone come to know with confidence that Christ lives in his or her heart by faith? Have any been experiencing deeper and wider dimensions of Christ's love, with the result that they are becoming more and more like Christ? What are some ways you have seen God answer? List the evidence in the margin.**

In the second part of his prayer, Paul became more specific and more pragmatic. He also became more intense. He said he was kneeling to pray. When Jews prayed, they ordinarily stood before the Lord. However, when they felt deeply about the content and object of their prayers, they fell on their knees. This indicates, of course, how deeply Paul, now a Christian, was exercised in his own heart about these believers. He truly wanted them to know and experience the realities of what it means to be a Christian.

AN INTENSE PRAYER

_____

_____

_____

➤10. **Have you ever become so intense in your praying for others that your heart and emotions were deeply moved?** ❏ Yes  ❏ No  ❏ I don't remember.

**If you have, can you remember for whom or what you were praying? Briefly describe one instance in the margin.**

🙏 Kneel down and pray to your heavenly Father. Thank Him that you have access to Him and that you can come in freedom and confidence. Ask Him to teach you how to pray with His heart for people. Ask Him to guide your praying through His Spirit so that you will have the same intensity in your praying as He has in His concern for the people for whom you pray.

## PART 3: EXPERIENCING HIS POWER AND LOVE

**Request 3: Strengthened in Your Inner Being.** Paul was referring both to external power and internal power. There is an external power of God, "which he exerted in Christ when he raised him from the dead and seated him at his right hand in the heavenly realms" (Eph. 1:20). This is the same power that raised these Christians "up with Christ and seated [them] with him" (Eph. 2:6). This was also the power that God gave the apostles and other selected Christians in the early days of the church to work mighty miracles in order to bear witness to the fact that the gospel was true.

Paul, however, was also referring to internal power and strength that are released within our hearts and inner beings. This power is rooted in two sources. The first comes when we have assurance of our salvation through faith. This power is experienced when we truly know, understand, and comprehend how secure our position is in Christ. In this sense, the power is psychological and emotional strength that comes from being sure of our position in Christ.

➤11. What's one source of this internal power?

It comes when we have _____ of our salvation.

➤12. Can you say that you have experienced this internal power that comes from the assurance of your salvation?  ❑ Yes   ❑ No

**If you haven't yet come to experience that internal strength, ask God to bring you to that place through His Spirit.**

The second source of internal power relates directly to God's indwelling Spirit. Jesus promised, "You will receive power when the Holy Spirit comes on you; and you will be my witnesses . . ." (Acts 1:8). This power is related to knowledge and truth. The power of God's Spirit is released in our lives through our interaction with both the written Word (Scripture) and the living Word (Jesus Christ). And this leads to a specific reason for Paul's request:

**Reason 3: That Christ May Dwell in Your Hearts.** Jesus Christ was no longer visible when Paul wrote to these saints. Nevertheless, He was alive, and through His Spirit He was living in their hearts. To accept this reality requires faith. To be strong, faith must be based on facts—even though these facts reflect invisible realities. The writer of Hebrews stated that "faith is being sure of what we hope for and certain of what we do not see" (Heb. 11:1).

The apostles and many other New Testament Christians saw Christ. They walked with Him, touched Him, and lived with Him. They saw Him die, and more important, they saw the undeniable evidence that He was raised from the dead. They heard Him speak of His return and then saw Him ascend to heaven.

The Ephesian Christians could only respond to what they heard about Christ. True, in the early days of the church, God bore witness to the message of Christ and salvation "by signs, wonders and various miracles, and gifts of the Holy Spirit" (Heb. 2:4). The Ephesians saw many of these "extraordinary miracles" (Acts 19:11-12). But the fact remains that Jesus was no longer visible. The temptation, particularly in the midst of persecution and difficulties, would be to grow weary and to waver spiritually. Thus, Paul prayed that the Ephesians would have an inner strength through the Word of God and through the ministry of God's Spirit to keep on believing and trusting the living Christ.

➤13. If you could make one request of God regarding your faith, what would it be? Check your response or write your own.
   ❑  a. Work through the faith You have given me to touch a lost world.
   ❑  b. Increase my faith so I will have more confidence and boldness.
   ❑  c. Strengthen my faith so I will quit wavering in my relationship with You.
   ❑  d. Give me faith to begin my relationship with You.

   ❑  e. Other: _____

**Request 4: Power to Grasp the Love of Christ.** To understand the full dimensions of Christ's love is a supernatural process. Human beings cannot understand that love apart from divine help and power. All the facts in the world can't help us truly understand it. In fact, Christ's love "surpasses knowledge." You can know all the facts in the Bible about His love, but God wants you to know experientially "how wide and long and high and deep is the love of Christ" (Eph. 3:18). Yet even then, we will never reach its full depth.

THE LOVE OF GOD
by F. M. Lehman

The love of God is greater far
Than tongue or pen
can ever tell.
It goes beyond the highest star,
And reaches to the lowest hell.
The guilty pair bowed
down with care
God gave His Son to win.
His erring child He reconciled,
And pardoned from his sin.

Could we with ink
the ocean fill,
And were the skies
of parchment made,
Were every stalk
on earth a quill,
And every man
a scribe by trade;
To write the love of God above
Would drain the ocean dry;
Nor would the scroll
contain the whole,
Though stretched
from sky to sky.

O love of God,
how rich and pure!
How measureless and strong.
It shall for evermore endure,
The saints' and angels' song.


1 Corinthians 13:4-7

"Love is patient, love is kind. It does not envy, it does not boast, it is not proud. It is not rude, it is not self-seeking, it is not easily angered, it keeps no record of wrongs. Love does not delight in evil but rejoices with the truth. It always protects, always trusts, always hopes, always perseveres."

➤14. **Read or sing (if you know the tune) the song in the margin about "The Love of God." As you read, think about the ways you have experienced His love.**

Paul also prayed "that you, being rooted and established in love, may have power, together with all the saints, to grasp" the full dimensions of Christ's love (Eph. 3:18). God placed us in the Body of Christ. We need each other. We're to love one another the way Christ loved us. Apart from the rest of the saints, we will never experience the fuller dimensions of Christ's love. We can only get to those depths with other believers. That's why we have encouraged you to complete this course of study with your minichurch. You can experience more of Christ's love together with them than you can alone.

➤15. **Where can you experience the fuller dimensions (height, depth, width, and length) of the love of Christ? Check the correct response.**

❑ a. I can experience more of Christ's love when I'm all alone with Him.

❑ b. I can experience more of Christ's love when I'm with other believers and we love one another the way Christ loved us.

**Reason 4: That You May Be Filled to the Fullness of God.** To be filled with God's fullness means being filled with "the knowledge of God" (Col. 1:10-11) and being "filled with the Spirit" (Eph. 5:18) as well. To be filled with the Spirit means you are fully surrendered to His control. The more you die to self, the more Christ is reflected in your life through His Spirit.

To the Colossians, Paul described the mystery as "Christ in you, the hope of glory" (Col. 1:27). He went on to say, "In Christ all the fullness of the Deity lives in bodily form, and you have been given fullness in Christ" (Col. 2:9-10). He explained that they were dead in sin, but "God made [them] alive with Christ" (Col. 2:13). He added, "Christ . . . is your life" (Col. 3:4). Jesus described this life that the Spirit would give as "streams of living water" that flow within those who have come to Christ (John 7:37-39).

Getting to know God better and experiencing His fullness is similar to what God intended to happen in marriage. In fact, in Ephesians 5, Paul used our relationship with Christ as Christians to illustrate the husband-wife relationship.

Many of us can remember those moments when we thought we were in love because of our emotional reactions. We call this infatuation. This kind of feeling is not wrong, nor is it necessarily something separate from true love. But this kind of "love" is not the basis upon which enduring marriages are built. Married life is not one continuing series of emotional highs. True love helps us endure the difficult times as well as the happy times. It does what's right even when we'd rather not.

The most complete definition of love is found in 1 Corinthians 13:4-7. This is the kind of stuff quality marriages are made of, the kind of love that endures and grows deeper. Unfortunately, some Christians have a relationship with God that's built more on infatuation than true love. They rely on emotional highs. They become confused when they don't feel good all the time. This, of course, is an unrealistic view of the Christian experience just as it is of marriage.

This is also a selfish approach to God. Some Christians are always asking, always wanting, always desiring more from God. They want Him to make them rich, heal their diseases, give them special gifts, and make them happy and successful. God does want to bless us. But He doesn't want us to have a one-sided, selfish love.

➤16. **How would you describe your love for God? Check the response closest to what you know is true of your love.**

❑ a. My love for God is focused more on what pleases Him. I want my life to please Him in everything I do.

❑ b. My love for God is focused on what He does for me. If He doesn't always do what I want, I'm not going to give Him my love.

When Paul prayed that these Christians may be "filled to the measure of all the fullness of God," he wasn't speaking of some ecstatic and supercharged emotional experience. It is true that this kind of knowledge will touch our emotions as well as our intellect. This is what leads us to worship God not only with our heads but also with our hearts. However, God designed a process of getting to know Him that should be ongoing and based on His will, not our pleasures.

Take time to express your love to the Lord. If He has revealed areas of your relationship with Him that need to grow and mature, ask Him to enable and empower you.

## PART 4: REVIEW AND PREVIEW

Congratulations! You've just completed your study of *Interacting with God in Ephesians 1–3*. We pray that this has been a valuable study for you and your minichurch. Though much of this letter has very practical applications for the believer, the content in the first three chapters is focused more on doctrine than application. Right living for the Christian always grows out of knowing the truth of God's Word. We've tried to help you understand that truth and, under the Holy Spirit's leadership, apply it to your life. Let's review. You may want to look back through your lessons to complete the following activities. If you started this course after the first lesson, you can skip the questions related to lessons you didn't study. For written responses, you may use the margin or a separate sheet of paper if you need more space.

➤17. **(Lessons 1-4) Review "Our Spiritual Blessings" in the margin. Of all these wonderful truths Paul described, which one has taken on new meaning or has been especially meaningful to you? Underline it.**

➤18. **(Lesson 5) Describe in the margin one way you have come to know God better during this study.**

➤19. **(Lessons 6-9) Which one (if any) of the following have you experienced in a new way or at a different depth because of this study? Check all that apply.**

❑ Hope                  ❑ God's Grace

❑ God's Power       ❑ Oneness in Christ

➤20. **Underline the one topic above by which your life has been affected most. Or underline the one topic you have the greatest need to experience. Describe the reason for your response in the margin.**

➤21. **(Lesson 10) What's one way you sense God has used you as a servant during this course, or what (if anything) do you sense He is calling you to as His servant?**

_____

➤22. **(Lesson 11) How has God revealed His glory to you or your minichurch during this course, or what do you sense He may be calling you to do (if anything) to reveal His glory in the Body of Christ in days to come? Write a note in the margin.**

---

OUR SPIRITUAL BLESSINGS

PART 1

• He chose us.

• He predestined us to be adopted as His children.

• He has freely given us His grace.

PART 2

• He redeemed us.

• He provided forgiveness for our sins.

• He lavished grace on us with all wisdom and understanding.

• He made known to us the mystery of His will.

PART 3

• He included us in Christ.

• He marked us in Christ with the Holy Spirit.

• He guaranteed our inheritance.

18. _____

_____

_____

20. _____

_____

_____

22. _____

_____

_____

23. _____

_____

_____

_____

24. _____

_____

_____

_____

➤23. In your minichurch meetings during the past 12 weeks, what one experience do you think most nearly reflects what God wants the Body of Christ to be like in the relationships between members?

➤24. What one thing do you believe your minichurch could do differently to better experience the closeness and love of the Body of Christ? Write a note in the margin.

 Spend a few minutes with your heavenly Father:
   • Thank Him for all He has revealed to you about Himself and His work in your life. "Count your many blessings."
   • Thank Him for the things He has allowed you to experience together with your brothers and sisters in Christ in your minichurch.
   • Ask the Lord to continue His work in your life and your church in such a way that your living will bring glory to Him and His Son.

➤25. If you have reached this point and you have a serious question about whether you have a personal saving relationship with Jesus Christ, turn back and review Parts 2 and 3 in the introduction (pp. 8-13), and let God bring you into that relationship today.

**Interacting with God in Ephesians 4–6.** Now that you have finished studying Ephesians 1–3, you have a wonderful foundation for the last half of the letter. The last three chapters of Ephesians (4–6) are focused much more on the applications of God's truth to right living. Paul wanted the saints to live a worthy life. He introduced the final half of his letter this way: "As a prisoner for the Lord, then, I urge you to live a life worthy of the calling you have received" (Eph. 4:1). The second *Interacting with God* workbook on Ephesians is a practical guide to help you and your minichurch live worthy lives for Christ individually, in your marriages, in your families, in your work life, in your church, and in the world. We trust that you will decide to continue your study of Ephesians by moving into *Interacting with God in Ephesians 4–6.*

➤26. **Read through the lesson titles from *Interacting with God in Ephesians 4–6.* Check the top <u>three</u> topics that would be of special interest to you.**
   ❏ 1. Living for God's Glory      ❏ 7. Living as Children of Light
   ❏ 2. Living a Worthy Life        ❏ 8. Living Carefully
   ❏ 3. Living in Unity             ❏ 9. Living for Christ in Your Marriage
   ❏ 4. Living in Christ's Body     ❏ 10. Living for Christ in Your Family
   ❏ 5. Living a Transformed Life   ❏ 11. Living for Christ in Your Vocation
   ❏ 6. Living a Life of Love       ❏ 12. Living in Christ's Strength

In his letters to the Ephesians (Eph. 1:17-19 and 3:16-19), Colossians (Col. 1:9-14), and Philippians (Phil. 1:9-11), Paul prayed for the saints. The following prayer is based on his prayers. You may want to copy this prayer and use it periodically in your personal time with God.

 **Close your study by praying the following prayer for yourself. As time permits, use the same topics to pray for your family and your church.**
   **Glorious Father,**
   • Please grant me spiritual wisdom and understanding.
   • Fill me with the knowledge of Your will so that I may know You better.
   • May my heart be enlightened so that I may know the hope to which You have called me; the hope that's based in Your grace and love that chose me in Christ Jesus before the creation of the world; the hope that is based on the same

power that raised Jesus Christ from the dead and seated Him at Your right hand.

• I pray that You'll strengthen me with Your power through Your Spirit in my inner being so that Christ may dwell in my heart through faith.

• Together with other saints, may I have power to grasp how wide and long and high and deep Christ's love for me really is.

• May I know this love that surpasses knowledge so that I may be filled to the measure of the fullness of God.

• All this I pray, Father, that I may live a life worthy of You and may please You in every way.

• As I grow in my knowledge of You, may I bear fruit in every good work.

• Grant that I may have endurance and patience and joyfully give thanks to You, Father, for my position in Christ.

> "Now to him who is able to do immeasurably more than all we ask or imagine, according to his power that is at work within us, to him be glory in the church and in Christ Jesus throughout all generations, for ever and ever! Amen" (Eph. 3:20-21).

# MINICHURCH MEETING 12

## BEFORE THE MEETING

❑ 1. Turn to "Preparing for Your Minichurch Meeting" on page 143. Use it as a guide to get ready for this meeting. Check the box above after you have prepared.

❑ 2. Unless God should direct otherwise, your minichurch leader will be using the following outline to guide your meeting. You may want to look over the questions and activities so you will be better prepared to participate.

## DURING THE MEETING

### ❖ Opening Prayer

### ❖ Singing Together

Consider singing "Sweet Hour of Prayer," "Higher Ground," or "The Love of God" together with other choruses and hymns.

### ❖ Building Relationships

Volunteers: What is one way you have experienced God's love as a part of this minichurch study over the past 12 weeks?

### ❖ Responding to God in Prayer

Stand and join hands in a circle. Using conversational prayer, thank God for the ways He has revealed Himself and allowed you to experience His love during the past 12-week study. Let everyone pray who wants to pray.

### ❖ Interacting with the Scriptures (in fours or sixes)

1. What verse or passage of Scripture has been most meaningful or challenging to you this week? How has God used it to speak to you? What significant actions have you taken this week because of something God revealed through His Word?

2. (p. 126) Volunteers: Recite the memory verse you have learned this week and explain any special meaning you have gained from it.

3. (p. 126, #5) What word or phrase from Ephesians 3:14-19 have you come to better understand or experience this week? Describe your understanding or experience.

### ❖ Reviewing the Lesson

1. (pp. 127-128) What are the four requests and the corresponding reasons in Paul's prayer for the church in Ephesians 1:17-19 and 3:16-19?

2. (pp. 128-129) What did Paul mean when he asked God to strengthen the Christians in their inner being?

3. (p. 130) Why can you experience more of Christ's love with other believers than you can alone?

4. (p. 130) What would it mean for you to be filled with the fullness of God?

### ❖ Applying the Truths to Life

1. (pp. 127-128, #7 and #9) How have you seen God answer these prayer requests the past 12 weeks?

2. (p. 128, #10) Volunteers: Describe a time when you experienced an intense time of prayer for others.

3. (p. 129, #13) Volunteers: What request would you make of God regarding your faith, and why?

4. (p. 130) How can our love for God be compared to love between a husband and wife in marriage? What makes for a lasting love relationship in marriage? What kind of love does God desire?

### ❖ Reviewing the Course

1. As time permits, share your responses to questions 17-24 on pages 131-132. If you need to, divide into fours or sixes for questions 17-22. Share #23 and #24 with your entire minichurch.

2. What's the most significant action you've taken or the most meaningful experience you've had because of our study of Ephesians 1–3?

### ❖ Praying for One Another (in fours or sixes)

One person at a time: What do you sense is the most important thing God wants you to do as a result of this study? How can we pray for you as you seek to obey Him? (Group: pray for this request, then move to the next person.)

### ❖ Previewing Ephesians 4–6

1. (p. 132, #26) What three topics in *Interacting with God in Ephesians 4–6* would be of special interest to you?

2. Discuss the desires of the group concerning continuing the study of Ephesians in this next workbook. Make plans about your next meeting.

3. Evaluate the size of your group. Have you grown to the point that you could multiply into two or more groups for this next course?

### ❖ Ministering to One Another

What needs (if any) of members have you become aware of during this meeting that the Body needs to care for? What can we do to meet the needs or to help connect the person with those who can help? Are there things we need to do this week to help?

### ❖ Reaching Out to Others

1. Are there persons in our circles of influence who might be ready to join our study of Ephesians 4–6? Whom are we praying for that we could pray for together?

2. Does anyone sense a calling to reach out to a whole new group of members by starting a new minichurch study of Ephesians 1–3?

### ❖ Closing Prayer
### ❖ Optional: "Breaking Bread" Together

# Minichurch Leader's Guide

The following guide is for those who will lead a small-group study of *Interacting with God in Ephesians 1–3*. If you haven't already done so, first read "Welcome" and "Introduction to Interacting with God," beginning on page 4. Then the remainder of this guide will make more sense to you.

## I. USING BACK TO THE BIBLE CURRICULUM RESOURCES

Back to the Bible began in 1939 primarily as a radio Bible-teaching ministry. To continue leading people into a dynamic relationship with God, the ministry has expanded to include the publication of curriculum resources for use with small groups. These small-group Bible studies are being developed as a service to the local church to help you experience the full dimensions of being a healthy Body of Christ.

### Goals

We have two goals for those who study these resources:

1. You will understand what God is saying to you in the Bible text studied, and you'll experience an increasingly intimate love relationship with Him.
2. Together with other Christians, you'll grow in your love for one another and increasingly become a healthy and mature Body of Christ that brings glory to God.

"All Scripture is God-breathed and is useful for teaching, rebuking, correcting and training in righteousness, so that the man of God may be thoroughly equipped for every good work" (2 Tim. 3:16-17). But we want to help Christians go beyond a head knowledge of God's Word into a personal love relationship with Him. Each workbook is designed to help people interact with God in a meaningful and dynamic relationship.

We also have a burden to assist churches in experiencing all that God has in mind for a healthy Body of Christ. These curriculum resources are designed to be used with small groups to help believers experience the fellowship (*koinonia*), love, and unity God intends for every church. We're calling these small groups "minichurches" to help people keep in mind that they need to function as the church to one another. They are "little churches within the church," or the church in miniature.

We've made every effort to focus the Bible teaching and church experience on the generally accepted teachings and practices of evangelical Christians. That way, Christians from many denominations will be able to benefit from sound Bible teaching and make applications within their own traditions. Teaching that's distinctive to your denomination can be added during the minichurch meetings if desired.

### Language Resources

Back to the Bible has an international ministry in many languages. We're committed to making these discipleship resources available to the nations and peoples of the world. Therefore, we are setting aside funds from English-language sales in the United States to provide for translation and publication of these resources in other languages. If you have an interest in resources in a particular language, contact us at 1-888-559-7878.

### Getting Ready

Follow your church's procedure for the approval of small-group curriculum. Some churches may have many groups meeting at different times and using a variety of resources. Other churches may want all their groups to use the same resource so the message and theme can be tied together with worship services and testimony times. In such cases, a pastor may even want to develop and preach his messages around the same scriptures or themes as those being studied in the minichurches. Use the following suggestions to prepare for your study.

**1. Pray.** God has a divine plan and purpose for your congregation. He wants to be Lord and head of His church. So begin your preparations in prayer. Trust the Lord to guide you every step of the way. Continue praying throughout the preparations and study to assure that you stay on God's agenda.

**2. Determine Time and Place for Minichurches.** Minichurches may go by any name for a small group. You already may have existing Sunday school classes, cell groups, discipleship groups, home Bible studies, and so forth that will use this study during their existing schedule. Consider offering as many options as possible to maximize participation. Groups can meet at church, in homes, in workplaces (before or after work or during lunch), in community meeting rooms, at restaurants, or in any number of other locations. The important factor is having a place that's relatively quiet and free of interruption. Groups can meet at any time that would be most convenient for participants. To have time for adequate discussion and praying together, we recommend one and a half to two hours for the meetings. Less time is still workable, but the depth of discussion will be limited.

**3. Enlist participants.** If small groups already exist, use the beginning of the study as an opportunity to encourage all members to join a small group. If members are not already participating in small groups, offer the chosen study to your congregation. Promote the study in ways that are already familiar to your church. The support and verbal promotion of the senior pastor will be a valuable part of encouraging participation.

**4. Form Minichurches.** Plan to divide those interested in the study into small groups or minichurches. To allow for the development of close and caring relationships, we recommend that your small groups have from 6 to 12 members. As they grow, you will want to have plans in place to multiply the groups in order to keep each group small. If you must work with a large group in a large room, plan on dividing into smaller groups of the same 6-12 people each week. You'll need a leader for each smaller group. (See section III on the next page for more details.)

**5. Enlist/Appoint Leaders.** The leaders don't have to be content experts since people will be studying the content during the week. The leaders, however, do need to be spiritually mature. They need to be people of prayer. They need to have a sensitivity to the needs of others and be able to lead small-group sessions that will help to build strong relationships. This guide and the weekly minichurch meeting plans will help. Choose a group leader for each minichurch. You also may want to select an apprentice for each group in consultation with the leader. (See section III on the next page for more details.)

**6. Order Resources.** The workbooks are available from Back to the Bible Publishing by calling 1-888-559-7878. Since you will need larger-than-normal quantities, place your orders several weeks in advance of your planned starting time.

**7. Set and Collect Fees.** Some churches may provide for the cost of workbooks through their regular church budget. Others may ask members to make a commitment to the study by paying for some or all of their workbooks. If you charge for workbooks, make sure to provide leaders with an anonymous "scholarship" option so that money will not limit participation by anyone. If members invite nonmembers and especially non-Christians to participate, we recommend that the member or the group provide workbooks to these as a ministry of the minichurch.

**8. Conduct an Introductory Minichurch Meeting.** Since participants need to complete homework before minichurch meeting 1, hold an introductory meeting to overview the study and provide workbooks to all participants. Suggestions for this meeting are on p. 140.

## Evaluate Your Progress

Your church leaders will want to guide and monitor the use of this curriculum. The following questions can help you think through the effectiveness of the minichurches and these resources. Take time at the end of each workbook study to ask:

- Are we living the reality of what God has created us to be? Are we growing strong in our faith?
- Are we growing in our experience of unity in the Body?
- Are we growing in our expressed love for one another?
- Are members becoming increasingly victorious over temptation and sin? Is holiness becoming more evident in their lives and lifestyle?
- Are we bringing glory to God as others see the Christ-likeness in us? Is God being glorified because of what He has done in us?
- Are people praising God and thanking Him for our lives? Are people coming to faith in Jesus?
- Are we being filled up to the fullest measure with the fullness of God? Are we growing stronger as a church?

## II. The Functions of a Minichurch

In His mission statement for the church in Matthew 28:19-20, Jesus described two foundational functions: (1) evangelism: Make disciples of all peoples; and (2) edification: Teach these new disciples to obey all that I have commanded. These two functions are priorities for every part of the church.

The writer to the Hebrews said, "Let us consider how we may spur one another on toward love and good deeds. Let us not give up meeting together, as some are in the habit of doing, but let us encourage one another" (Heb. 10:24-25). Paul said to the Galatians, "Carry each other's burdens, and in this way you will fulfill the law of Christ" (Gal. 6:2). In 1 Corinthians 12 and Romans 12, the church is described as the Body of Christ. As members of this body, we need one another to be complete. So we need to be in loving, caring relationships with one another. Every church needs to maintain a healthy balance between

1. learning experiences with God's Word,
2. relational experiences with one another, and
3. witnessing experiences with non-Christians.

Many churches today don't have a place where members really get to know, love, and care for one another. They may have small classes for Bible study or discipleship, but those are often places for gaining information rather than experiencing and practicing the life of the Body of Christ. Consequently, people who are broken and hurting don't have a place to share their burdens in a setting where others will help them carry those burdens. Every church needs that kind of opportunity for every member.

As stated earlier, a minichurch is "a little church within the church." It's a church in miniature. It may go by many different names, but it's a small group of believers who seek to live as the Body of Christ to one another. A minichurch needs to maintain the healthy balance described above. In developing this series of curriculum resources, we've tried to provide tools that will help do that.

In this small-group setting, members can get to know one another well enough that they can bear one another's burdens, confess faults and sins, rebuke, exhort, admonish, and minister to one another with the Word.

A minichurch is also a place where outsiders can come and see how we love one another and show ourselves to be Jesus' disciples. When a minichurch is healthy, the unique unity of the Body of Christ is revealed in such a way that people are convinced that Jesus is the divine Son of God. A minichurch is an ideal setting to have a practical balance between edification, relationships, and evangelism.

A minichurch, however, needs the larger body. There's a place for the celebration, worship, and preaching/teaching ministry that takes place in that setting. When a church really takes the matter of love seriously, it will find many who have needs. The larger the body, the greater possibility that resources to meet the needs are already present.

By structuring to function in a large setting and also in minichurches, we believe a church can begin to experience greater dimensions of what God intends for a healthy Body of Christ. We offer this curriculum to you with the prayer that you will experience "together with all the saints . . . how wide and long and high and deep is the love of Christ, and to know this love that surpasses knowledge—that you may be filled to the measure of all the fullness of God" (Eph. 3:18-19).

For more information about the functioning of a church (and minichurch), we recommend *The Walk: The Measure of Spiritual Maturity*, by Gene Getz (Nashville: Broadman and Holman, 1994), and *Body Life*, by Ray C. Stedman (Ventura, Calif.: Regal Books, 1972).

## III. THE MINICHURCH LEADERSHIP TEAM

Since minichurches can take different forms in different churches, you need to feel free to develop the leadership structure in the ways that are best for you. Limiting the size of the groups also will limit the number and giftedness of available leaders. You can be very flexible in developing your structure according to your needs and available people. If you're starting groups for the first time, or if you wish to restructure your existing groups, you may want to consider these suggestions. We recommend two primary leadership positions and then describe some optional positions.

**Leader.** The leader is a spiritual facilitator for the minichurch. As mentioned earlier, he does not have to be a content expert, but he does need to be a spiritually mature person. He will guide the members to function as the Body of Christ to one another even though they're only "a little church within the church." This person should prayerfully consider God's call to this position because of the high responsibility involved in leading God's people (James 3:1).

The leader should assume primary guidance of the team members described below. He should prayerfully direct the sessions each week and involve the leader apprentice on occasion to develop his or her skills. He should become familiar with the suggestions for leading a minichurch meeting in the following section, then follow the Lord's direction in leading the weekly meetings. Together with the rest of the team and under the Lord's direction, he should help the minichurch to multiply into two groups when the size requires it.

**Leader Apprentice.** The apprentice should be chosen in consultation with the minichurch leader. He or she is a leader in training. The two should work together closely in praying for the minichurch, planning for the meetings, evaluating progress, and ministering to members as needs arise. On occasion, the apprentice should lead some or all of the meetings in order to get experience.

As your minichurch grows, it will need to multiply to two groups so the groups stay small enough for members to maintain spiritual intimacy with one another. When this multiplication occurs, half of the group will go with the leader, and the apprentice will become leader of the other half. Because relationships already will be established between the members and the apprentice, this transition will go much smoother. Once a minichurch multiplies, each of the new groups will secure a new apprentice.

**Optional: Host/Hostess.** The host or hostess can assist the leader by preparing the room, providing name tags, and greeting and introducing visitors and new group members. He or she also would coordinate the provision of light refreshments if desired. When your minichurch has a meal together, the host/hostess would coordinate that also. This person should have the gift of hospitality and a willingness to be a servant to the minichurch. You may even want to select a husband-and-wife team to serve in this role.

**Optional: Music Leader and/or Musician.** One segment of the minichurch meeting calls for singing hymns and choruses together. This can be a meaningful time of worship and preparing hearts for the remainder of the meeting. The leader or apprentice can direct this time, or you can enlist a music leader.

The minichurch meeting plans at the end of each lesson give a few suggestions. If needed, he or she would secure hymnals or songbooks for use. If overheads or handouts are used, be sure you have proper permissions or license to reproduce copyrighted material. If special music is desired on occasion (either live or recorded), the music leader would make the arrangements.

You also may need a musician if an instrument is desired. Many small groups may be limited in the availability of a musician. In that case, the group may want to sing a cappella or use a sing-along tape or compact disc.

## IV. Leading a Minichurch Meeting

The following suggestions should help you in planning for and conducting the minichurch meetings each week:

**Pray.** As a spiritual leader, you need to make prayer a primary part of your work. Prayer grows out of a relationship with Jesus, who is head of His church. You need His direction as you guide His people to respond to Him. Spend time each week praying for each of your group members and their needs. As you have opportunity with individuals, don't just say "I'll pray for you," but do it right there. Praying in the presence of the person is a special ministry to him or her.

**Minichurch Meeting Plans.** After each lesson, a page is dedicated to plans for the minichurch meeting where you will process together what you've learned during the week. The plan for the first meeting is on page 24. These plans are provided for everyone for several reasons. First, you don't have to do a great deal of preparation to get ready to lead the meeting. You can be a learner right along with everyone else. Second, members can review the plans and make sure they're prepared for the meeting. Those who may be shy when asked to say something spontaneously will be able to think about what they want to relate. Then the sharing time will be more meaningful. Third, members will realize they need to do their lessons prior to the meeting. Fourth, if for some reason you're not able to attend, your apprentice or any member of the group can take over at a moment's notice. Fifth, when you divide into smaller groups, each small group will have instructions to follow. And finally, if a person doesn't hear a question or instruction clearly, he or she will be able to read it without embarrassment.

**General Time Schedule.** You'll need to vary the amount of time devoted to each activity from week to week. If your group is talkative, you probably won't be able to do every-thing no matter how hard you try. You'll benefit from deciding beforehand about how much time to allow for each activity, and then be ready to adjust if needed. Generally, we suggest that you divide your time in the following ways:

- ¼ Singing and building relationships
- ½ Interacting with the Scriptures, reviewing the lesson, and applying the truths
- ¼ Praying, ministering to one another, and reaching out

**Following God's Agenda.** The goal of this study, however, is not to cover the content. Nor is it to make sure you conduct every activity suggested in the minichurch meeting plans. The primary goal is to help God's people interact with God and one another around God's Word. As this happens, God will help His people become all that He desires them to be. As the leader, you need to be spiritually prepared to guide the minichurch according to God's agenda. We've designed this curriculum to allow you to do this with great freedom.

Each week, minichurch members will be covering the content in-depth as they study their lesson. They'll be interacting with God and making personal application as we guide them in their Bible study. This way you won't have to feel pressured to cover all the content in the meeting before the time is up. You can give God permission to interrupt your meeting at any time. You can focus on relationships and the needs of members.

Most weeks, you'll probably follow the meeting plans at the end of each lesson. These plans have a balance of discussing content and application together with building relationships. However, you may come to a meeting and find that one member is facing a crisis. In a case like that, you can set aside the meeting plans and spend time with the group offering comfort, counsel, and prayer. If you have time to get back to the plans, fine. If you don't, that's okay too.

Another week, your group may be overwhelmed with a sense of God's presence and work in your lives. You may spend more of the time worshiping the Lord in singing, prayer, and testimony. In another meeting, someone may realize for the first time that he has never been saved. You can take time to lead him to Christ right there in front of the minichurch—and oh, what rejoicing there will be!

As the leader, you need to be sensitive to what God wants to do with the group members. Be alert to times when He may want you to give greater emphasis to one of the following: Bible study, prayer, fellowship and relationship building, testimonies, worship, ministry to one another, or discussing outreach to a person, family, or group.

**Name Tags.** We recommend that you wear name tags every week. We encourage group members to invite visitors or new participants to the minichurch meeting. Even though the regular members will get to know each other quickly, new people need to feel comfortable as well. They will be able to blend in much more quickly if they can learn names without embarrassment. Secure relatively heavy-duty name tags from an office supply store. Prepare a name tag for each participant, and make extras available for visitors. Between meetings, store the name tags at your meeting place (if possible). Assign a person to collect all the name tags before members dismiss each week so they won't be forgotten and left at home for the next meeting.

**Singing Together.** If you choose to sing together, allow about ten minutes for it. Occasionally you may want to prepare special music, either live, via cassette or CD, or using a Christian music video. If members seem to want to sing more, you may want to take a break one week and hold a songfest. Otherwise, limit the amount of singing to maximize your time for interacting with God and one another through the Word.

**Building Relationships.** We want your minichurch participants to get well acquainted. They need to know one another and care about each other. So in each meeting plan, we've included some suggestions for people to talk about themselves and their lives. You may use these, adapt them, or develop your own. You'll need to watch the time to allow time for other activities. Don't feel as if everyone must speak every week. Be prepared to gently "encourage" a person to bring his story to a close if he begins to go too long.

**Optional Retreat.** One way to speed up the getting-acquainted stage is to conduct a half-day, whole-day, or weekend retreat to kick off the study. Develop a list of questions or discussion starters to guide the members to tell each other about themselves, their families, their work, and their walk with the Lord. Include some time for prayer, worship, and fun too.

**Praying Together.** During the times we encourage you to pray for one another, we recommend you divide into groups of fours or sixes. This is so you'll be able to pray for each individual and his or her needs. If members have difficulty praying in the smaller groups, you may want to keep the group together in the early meetings until the members begin to develop their praying skills. If you have some skilled intercessors, you may want to assign them to different small groups so that each group can experience an effective prayer time.

**Testimonies.** A number of the activities in the meeting plans call for testimonies of some kind about personal experiences with God. God, however, will probably be working in ways that produce testimonies the lesson plans don't call for. Watch and listen for ways God is working in the lives of individuals. When you become aware of these, invite a person to give a testimony of what God is doing. If you have a question about whether he or she will be willing to speak, privately ask for permission to call on him or her.

**Ministering to One Another.** The testimony of the early church was that there were no poor people because members shared with each other whenever one had a need (Acts 4:32-35). This kind of sharing is a natural by-product of a love relationship with God and one another. This is the real evidence that you're experiencing *koinonia* (loving fellowship). Your minichurch may not be able to meet all the needs that arise. However, you can undergird, support, and seek to connect a person with the things needed to meet his need. Your whole church may have or want to develop ways for members who "have" to share with those who "need."

**Reaching Out.** As your group matures as a loving and caring community, members will want to invite others. Though it would be nice for a person to study this book from the beginning, we have attempted to write the lessons so they can stand alone. That way, members can invite new people at any time. You don't have to limit your group to Christians only, either. Non-Christians who are willing to participate will have a wonderful opportunity to see the difference Jesus makes in a life. Their openness to the Bible study probably indicates that God is drawing them to Himself through His Son.

Encourage members, therefore, to invite others. As mentioned earlier, we suggest that you give a book to those who want to participate in the remainder of the study. You'll want to briefly overview the workbook and study process for newcomers after the meeting. Encourage them to read the introduction and the lesson for the coming week.

**"Breaking Bread" Together.** One of the activities of the early church was the breaking of bread together from house to house. It became known as a love feast. This was more than just observing the Lord's Supper. Likewise, your minichurch may want to "break bread" together from time to time. This might include light refreshments every week. However, you also may want to plan for a full meal together. This could be in conjunction with your minichurch meeting (before or after) or at another time during the week. Be careful, however, not to let members get into a competition over refreshments or food.

**Minichurch Covenant.** A covenant is an agreement between two or more parties. We've suggested a covenant for your minichurch on page 144. The introductory minichurch meeting includes a time for "agreeing together" using the covenant. Prepare to guide the participants in adding to, deleting, or otherwise revising the agreement so they can agree with one another about it. Review the covenant during the first few meetings. Then mention the agreements in future meetings if you sense a reminder is needed. If a new person joins the study, you might want to privately review the covenant with him or her.

**Conduct an Introductory Minichurch Meeting.** Follow these suggestions in preparing for and conducting the introductory meeting:

❑ 1. Review the items under "Getting Ready" on pp. 135-36. Complete any of those preparations that have not been done.

❑ 2. If possible, provide copies of the book to all participants, and ask them to read the introduction (pp. 5-13) prior to the introductory minichurch meeting.

❑ 3. Provide a name tag (temporary for this meeting or the more permanent ones described above) for each participant. Provide markers for the name tags, index cards, and extra pencils or pens.

❑ 4. Read through the meeting plans on page 14, and prepare to guide the meeting. Feel free to customize the meeting agenda any way you sense would be best. These plans should serve as "suggestions" or a starting point. They should not be seen as a rigid and unchangeable agenda.

❑ 5. You need to be prepared to describe and explain each of the items listed under "Minichurch Leader's Overview." If members have already had a chance to read the introduction, this can be a brief review.

❑ 6. If you have too many participants for one minichurch, work with your church leaders to start the number of minichurches needed to keep the groups small. We recommend 6-12. If you have 16-20 or more, you probably should consider starting a new group.

❑ 7. During the meeting, collect the information cards participants have prepared. You may want to get permission to provide this information to the whole group so members can stay in touch with one another during the study. If you get permission, you can prepare the information for distribution at the next meeting.

❑ 8. If people have not had time to read the introduction prior to this meeting, ask them to try to read it (especially Parts 2 and 3) in addition to Lesson 1 for next week.

# GLOSSARY

The following definitions have been used in the lessons for Ephesians 1–3. The numbers in parentheses correspond to the numbering system used in "Dictionary of the Greek Testament" in *Strong's Exhaustive Concordance of the Bible*. For a more detailed study of New Testament words, you may want to get a copy of *Vine's Expository Dictionary of New Testament Words*.

**administration:** (3622) stewardship, dispensation, management, oversight of household or estate.

**adopted:** (5206) placed in position as a son (child).

**apostle(s):** (652) a delegate, messenger, one that is sent, an ambassador of the gospel, a commissioner of Christ; usually refers to the 12 disciples who had been close to Jesus throughout His ministry, and later to Paul by special call of Christ.

**authority:** (1849) one with delegated influence, jurisdiction, rule of government.

**believe:** (4100) to have faith in, upon, or with respect to; to entrust one's spiritual well-being to Christ, commit, trust.

**blameless:** (299) without blame, unblemished, faultless, unblameable.

**blessed:** (2127) invoke a benediction upon, bless, praise, cause to prosper or make happy.

**blessings:** (2129) benefits.

**boast:** (2744) claim credit, take glory for self.

**called:** (2821) to summon, to appoint for a particular destiny.

**chief cornerstone:** (204) foundation stone placed at the corner and around which a building is constructed.

**chosen:** (2820) selected as a kindness or favor.

**Christ:** (5547) the Messiah, the anointed One.

**church:** (1577) the whole community of Christians, all saints both in heaven and on earth.

**circumcision:** (4061) people who prided themselves in following the religious ritual (given by God to Abraham) of removing the foreskin of all males.

**citizen:** (4847) native of the same town, co-religionist, one who has a home alongside of others in a holy nation.

**confidence:** (4006) reliance, trust.

**covenants of the promise:** (1242, 1860) God's commitments to Abraham and the patriarchs to bless the world through their descendants by sending a Savior.

**deposit:** (728) earnest, a pledge given in advance as security for the rest.

**discouraged:** (1573) faint, weak, weary, failing in heart.

**dividing wall of hostility:** (3320, 5418) fence, enclosing barrier, partition, the Mosaic regulations that kept Jews separate from Gentiles.

**dominion:** (2963) mastery, one who possesses rulership over others.

**enlightened:** (5461) to shed rays, to illuminate, make to see, instruct.

**established:** (2311) grounded, settled, foundation laid, consolidated.

**eternal:** (165) for evermore, without end, continued duration.

**eyes:** (3788) (figuratively) your vision, sight, the channel for knowing.

**faith:** (4102) reliance upon Jesus for salvation, trust, constancy in relationship to Jesus, loyalty to Jesus, continuing to trust in Jesus, fidelity.

**faithful:** (4103) trustworthy, trustful, believing, sure, true.

**family:** (3965) descendants from the same father, kindred.

**forgiveness:** (859) to carry or send away, to be gracious toward, to let loose.

**freedom:** (4318) access, admission.

**generations:** (1074) ages of time or people.

**Gentiles:** (1484) non-Jews, pagans, heathen.

**gift:** (1431) something given, a gratuity.

**gift:** (1435) a present, something given freely.

**glorious:** (1391) full of glory, splendor, dignified, honorable, praiseworthy.

**glory:** (1391) evidence of God's wonderful work or character, honor.

**gospel:** (2098) a good message, good news.

**grace:** (5485) graciousness, the divine influence upon the heart and its reflection in the life, acceptable, undeserved favor, free gift.

**grasp:** (2638) comprehend, perceive, seize possession of.

**head:** (2776) supreme, chief, most prominent.

**heart:** (1271) or mind, deep thought, understanding, the whole of one's inner being.

**heart:** (2588) thoughts, feelings.

**heavenly realms:** (2032) the heavenlies, above the sky, celestial, in heaven.

**heirs:** (4789) co-heirs, participants in common.

**holy:** (40) sacred, pure, blameless, consecrated.

**hope:** (1680) to anticipate with pleasure, confident expectation.

**hope:** (4267) confident expectation, assurance of what is to come.

**household:** (3609) a relative, member of the family, children with one Father.

**immeasurably more:** (5228, 1537) exceeding abundantly, superior to.

**incomparably:** (5235) without comparison, beyond the usual, surpassing.

**inheritance:** (2817) possessions given to heirs, eternal blessedness.

**inner being:** (2080, 444) (inner man) inside, inward part of a person.

**insight:** (4907) knowledge, understanding, intelligence.

**intent:** (2443) plan, desire.

**Israel:** (2474) descendants of Israel (Jacob), the nation chosen by God to be His people.

**Jesus:** (2424) personal name meaning "Jehovah saves."

**kindness:** (5544) gentleness, goodness, excellence in character or demeanor.

**know:** (1492) be aware, have experiential knowledge of, perceive, be sure, understand.

**know:** (1922) fully discern, to become fully acquainted with, to gain intimate and experiential knowledge of.

**knowledge:** (1108) factual information, learning.

**law:** (3551) commands and regulations given by God to Moses and Israel.

**Lord:** (2962) supreme in authority, controller, Master.

**love:** (26) [*agape*] godly affection, benevolence, seeking the very best for another unconditionally.

**manifold:** (4182) with much variety, multifaceted.

**mercy:** (1656) pity, active compassion that meets needs.

**mystery:** (3466) a divine secret that has been or is being revealed.

**new man:** (2537, 444) a new creation, a new humanity including Jew and Gentile and all races in a mystical new Body of Christ.

**peace:** (1515) set at one, whole, prosperity, quietness, rest, the One bringing two parts together in oneness.

**possession:** (4047) something purchased, an acquisition.

**power:** (1411) miraculous force, might, strength, ability.

**praise:** (1868) laudation, commendation, a commendable thing.

**preach:** (2097) proclaim good news.

**predestine:** (4309) to limit or set out in advance, determine before.

**prisoner:** (1198) a captive, in bonds, one imprisoned.

**promise:** (1860) a pledge, a divine assurance of good.

**prophet:** (4396) foreteller, inspired speaker, one who brought God's messages to His people.

**purpose:** (4286) intention, proposal, a setting forth.

**reconcile:** (604) restore to right relationship, removal of offending sin.

**redemption:** (629) ransom in full from bondage, bought at a price and released, setting slaves of sin free to live for God.

**reveal:** (1107) make known, declare, give understanding.

**revelation:** (602) illumination, manifestation, appearing, uncovering.

**riches:** (4149) wealth, abundance, valuable bestowment.

**rooted:** (4492) stabilized.

**rule:** (746) one chief in rank, magistrate, leader.

**saints:** (40) sacred ones, ones set apart as holy, set apart for God, consecrated.

**sake:** (5228) in behalf of, in stead, on the part of.

**salvation:** (4991) rescue, safety, deliverance from the eternal penalty of death for sin.

**saved:** (4982) given eternal salvation, delivered, made whole.

**seal:** (4972) stamp with a signet or private mark for security or showing ownership.

**separate:** (5565) without, apart from, no relationship to.

**servant:** (1249) an attendant, one with menial duties, minister, deacon.

**sharer:** (4830) co-participant, partaker.

**sin:** (3900) a side-slip, deviation, error, offense, fault, missing the mark (also "transgressions").

**sins:** (266) missing of the mark, errors, wrongdoing.

**Spirit:** (4151) the divine Holy Spirit of God.

**spiritual:** (4152) not carnal, of the Spirit as opposed to the flesh.

**strengthen:** (2901) to empower, increase in vigor, to wax strong.

**sufferings:** (2347) tribulations, afflictions, burdens, troubles, persecution.

**surpasses:** (5235) beyond the usual mark, excel, pass, exceeding.

**temple:** (3485) the inner sanctuary where God dwells, a spiritual building.

**transgressions:** (3900) breaking the law, willfully crossing the line (also "sin").

**truth:** (225) that which is true, ultimate reality.

**uncircumcised:** (203) not circumcised according to the covenant God made with Abraham and his descendants, figuratively unregenerate, a derogatory name for Gentiles.

**understanding:** (5428) intellectual or moral insight, prudence.

**unsearchable:** (421) past finding out, untraceable.

**will:** (2307) a determination, choice, purpose, desire, inclination, pleasure.

**wisdom:** (4678) understanding the true nature of things.

**without hope:** (1680) no knowledge or expectation of salvation beyond this life.

**workmanship:** (4161) a product, that which is made.

**works:** (2041) acts, deeds, activities, actions.

**wrath:** (3709) thoughtful anger, indignation, judgment, vengeance.

# PREPARING FOR YOUR MINICHURCH MEETING

**I. Prayer.** Prior to your minichurch meeting this week, take time to pray about the following matters. You may want to make notes in a journal or on a separate sheet of paper. Ask God . . .

1. Do I love You with all my heart, soul, mind, and strength? Or am I giving too much love and attention to some person, possession, or activity? How can I adjust my life to be more in love with You?

2. Are any activities (even good things) in my life taking up too much time so that I can't do the most important things You desire from me? What would You like to "prune" from my life so I will be more fruitful (John 15:1-2)?

3. Are there any impurities of the world that need to be cleaned from my mind and life so I will be more holy and pure before You?

4. Do I need to confess, repent, and seek forgiveness for any sin that's keeping me from having close fellowship with You?

5. Do I have a broken relationship with another person that needs fixing? What should I do?

6. What, if anything, would You want me to pray or do for a brother or sister in Christ to help build up and strengthen the Body of Christ? Do any have needs that You would want to meet through me?

7. Are there people in my circle of influence who need a saving relationship with Jesus Christ? How can I pray for them, and what, if anything, would You have me do to show them Your love?

**II. Review.** Take a few minutes to review your lesson for this week. Then respond to the following questions or activities:

1. What Bible verse has been most meaningful, or which one has God used to speak to you in a special way?

2. Has God revealed anything to you through His Word that calls for obedience or response of some kind? What do you need to do?

3. What word or phrase from the focus scripture have you come to understand better? How is God guiding you to experience any of these concepts?

3. Practice reciting your Scripture memory verse for the week. Review the verses you've learned thus far in the course.

**III. Pay Attention to the Body.** Minichurch meetings are intended to be flexible and responsive to the leadership of the Holy Spirit. If you become aware of any of the following needs in one of the members, ask that person for permission to bring the need to the attention of the group leader. Let the individual know of your love and concern. Guard against revealing anything as gossip. Speak only out of love.

- Members who may be carrying a particularly heavy burden and need the prayer and ministry of the group.
- Crises facing one or more members that need a more extended time of intercessory prayer.
- Members who are struggling with temptation or sin and need to have the group pray for them according to James 5:13-20.

**IV. Self-Examination.** Take some time to reflect on your own life (individual, family). Are there things you need to discuss with an individual or with your group? Pride may cause you to keep quiet. Yet God may want to use the group to minister to you in a way that will cause you and the group to grow stronger. Consider the following questions, and reveal your needs to a close friend or your minichurch leader.

1. Where are you hurting? In what way do you feel needy? What load are you carrying that seems to be too heavy to bear?

2. Are you struggling to gain victory over sin or temptation of some kind? Does the Lord want you to practice James 5:16 ("Confess your faults one to another, and pray one for another, that ye may be healed," KJV)? If so, whom should you talk with? (Items of a sexual nature should only be discussed with a person of the same sex, and probably not in a group setting.)

3. Are there deep wounds, hurts, or offenses in your past that you need help with? Begin to ask the Lord about whom you should turn to for help. Don't try to carry such a heavy burden alone.

4. What's the most meaningful way your minichurch could pray for you?

**V. Rejoicing.** Paul encouraged members to "Rejoice with those who rejoice" (Rom. 12:15). Jesus told a man He had healed, "Return home and tell how much God has done for you" (Luke 8:39). Have you had a special experience with God that you need to relate to others? Has God blessed you in such a way that you need to give a witness to His goodness, faithfulness, or love? Ask the Lord to help you describe His activity in such a way that He gets the glory and the faith of others will increase. You may want to speak with your minichurch leader prior to the meeting so he or she will be able to decide where to include your testimony.

# INTERACTING WITH GOD

# MINICHURCH COVENANT

Believing that God wants His people to be a healthy Body of Christ with Jesus Christ Himself as its head, we submit ourselves to Him and to one another so that we may help each other grow into mature believers and so that, as a group, we "may be built up until we all reach unity in the faith and in the knowledge of the Son of God and become mature, attaining to the whole measure of the fullness of Christ" (Eph. 4:12-13). Together we agree to:

1. Study God's Word each week and complete the learning activities for the week's lesson prior to the minichurch meeting.

2. Pray regularly and specifically for one another, our church, our spiritual leaders, and those who need to come into a saving relationship with Jesus Christ.

3. Attend all minichurch meetings unless unavoidable circumstances prevent attendance. If we are unable to attend, we will make every effort to notify our minichurch leader and let him or her know how the group can pray for us in our absence.

4. Participate in the minichurch meetings by listening carefully and sharing openly.

5. Keep confidential any personal matters discussed by other members during the meetings.

6. Seek to demonstrate love as the Holy Spirit leads us to help meet one another's needs.

7. Seek to bring glory and honor to God through our relationships with one another.

Signatures:                                          Date:_____

_____        _____

_____        _____

_____        _____

_____        _____

_____        _____

_____        _____